Desk Copy - Mrs.

D1508296

MILL CREEK SCHOOL

The Music Hour

Fifth Book

by
Osbourne McConathy
Formerly Director of the Department of Public School Music, Northwestern University

W. Otto Miessner
Chairman, Department of School Music, School of Fine Arts, University of Kansas

Edward Bailey Birge
Professor of Public School Music, Indiana University

Mabel E. Bray
Director of Music, New Jersey State Teachers College
Trenton, New Jersey

Silver Burdett Company

New York   Boston   Chicago   San Francisco

ACKNOWLEDGMENTS

The courtesy of the following authors and publishers in allowing the use of copyrighted material is gratefully acknowledged:

D. Appleton and Company for the poems "March" and "To the Fringed Gentian" by William Cullen Bryant from *The Poetical Works of William Cullen Bryant;* Executors of the Estate of Katharine Lee Bates for "America, the Beautiful"; The Beacon Press, Inc., for the first verse of "Giving," from *The Beacon Song and Service Book.* Used with permission; Mr. Percival Chubb for the second stanza of "Giving"; The Churchman for the words "The Spirit of the Birch" by Reverend Arthur Ketchum; Mr. Bridgham Curtis for "Tawi' Kuruks" and "Wioste Olowan" from *The Indians' Book* by Natalie Curtis, copyright, 1907, by Natalie Curtis, copyright, 1923, by Paul Burlin, published by Harper and Brothers; Dodd, Mead & Company for "Spring Night" by Bliss Carman from *April Airs;* E. P. Dutton and Company, Inc., New York City, for "The Night Will Never Stay." Taken by permission from Farjeon's *Gypsy and Ginger,* published and copyrighted by E. P. Dutton and Company; Harper and Brothers for the poem "By the Waves" by Margaret E. Sangster; Houghton Mifflin Company for the following poems: "Leaves at Play" by Frank D. Sherman; "Morning-Glories" by Abbie Farwell Brown; "The Toadstool" by Oliver Wendell Holmes; "A Day of Sunshine" by Henry Wadsworth Longfellow; and "The Plaint of the Camel" by Charles Edward Carryl. Used by permission of and by arrangement with the publishers; The Ladies' Home Journal, Curtis Publishing Company, Philadelphia, Pa., for the poem "Time Enough" by Berton Braley. Reprinted by permission of the publishers; Mrs. Emma Endicott Marean for the poem "The Rhyme of the Country Road" from her collection of poems, *Now and Then;* James B. Pinker and Sons for "Dream Song" by Walter de la Mare, from *Peacock Pie,* published by Henry Holt and Company; G. P. Putnam's Sons for the poem "A Child's Book" by Charles Keeler from *Elfin Songs of Sunland;* G. Schirmer, Inc., for the melody "Tarantella" from *Songs of the People,* collected and edited by Eduardo Marzo; Miss Edith Sitwell for the poem "The King of China's Daughter"; Frederick A. Stokes Company for the poems "The Three Little Ships" and "The Traffic Man" by Annette Wynne from *For Days and Days, A Year-round Treasury of Verse for Children,* copyright, 1919; Henri Wehrmann for the use of "Misieu' Banjo." Miss Carolyn Wells for the poem "How to Tell Wild Animals," published by Harper and Brothers; Youth's Companion for the poem "The Snow" by Alice V. L. Carrick by permission of the author and publishers.

Grateful acknowledgment is due the following for permission to reprint copyrighted material:

D. Appleton and Company for "Beethoven in His Study" by Schloesser, "Robert Schumann," and "Tarantella" by Sinding, from *The Music of the Modern World* by Anton Seidl. Ewing Galloway, N. Y., for "Springtime in Normandy" by Burton Holmes. Rudolf Lesch for "The Old Watermill" by Hobbema, and "The Angelus" by Millet. The Metropolitan Museum of Art for the following: "In the Connecticut Hills" by Foster; "Roman Girl at a Fountain" by Bonnat; and "Jeanne d'Arc" by Bastien-Lepage. The Scituate Historical Society for "The Old Oaken Bucket Place" from a crayon drawing by Henry Turner Bailey.

Grateful acknowledgment is also due Dr. Emma Grant Meader, formerly instructor in Elementary Education, Teachers College, Columbia University, for her selection and supervision of the choice of poetry; Miss Mary Wood Hinman for her assistance in correlating rhythmic activities with the vocal music lesson; Mrs. Horatio Parker for permission to reproduce the photograph of Dr. Horatio Parker, and also for making available several of his compositions; Dr. Walter Van Dyke Bingham and Dr. Ben Wood for their collaboration in providing the sections "Why We Study Music" and "Questions for Thought and Discussion."

Piano accompaniments for the Fifth Book may be found in Teacher's Guide for the Fifth Book.

COPYRIGHT, 1930, 1937, BY

SILVER BURDETT COMPANY

PRINTED IN THE UNITED STATES OF AMERICA

To
America's distinguished composer
Horatio Parker
whose artistic contribution to
school music expressed his faith
in the musical future
of our people

Horatio Parker

The Music Hour

FIFTH BOOK

Morning-Glories
Reading Song

ABBIE FARWELL BROWN

HORATIO PARKER

Waltz Song

Be - fore I o - pen drow - sy eyes, The lit - tle
They wake so ear - ly in the day, That, as the

morn - ing - glo - ries rise *f* To climb their lad - ders
morn - ing wears a - way, They droop all sleep - y -

green and tall That lean up - on the gar - den wall. They
eyed; you see, I know, it is the same with me. Their

long to reach the top and find What sights are hid - den
heads be - gin to nod and swing, They can - not climb, they

there be - hind, But nev - er one can climb so high, They al - ways fail and
can - not cling, A - sleep they tum - ble off, and then They must be - gin to

this is why, And this is why:
climb a - gain, To climb a - gain.

1

Under the Window
Reading Song

KATE GREENAWAY

HORATIO PARKER

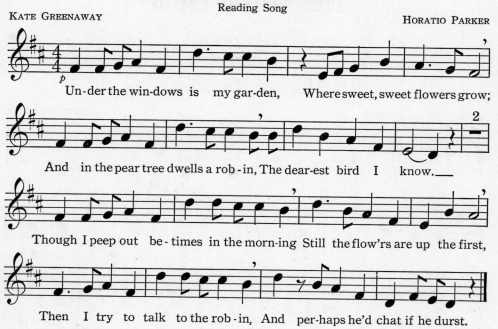

Un-der the win-dows is my gar-den, Where sweet, sweet flowers grow;

And in the pear tree dwells a rob-in, The dear-est bird I know.___

Though I peep out be-times in the morn-ing Still the flow'rs are up the first,

Then I try to talk to the rob-in, And per-haps he'd chat if he durst.

To a Humming Bird
Reading Song

JOHN VANCE CHENEY

ANNA VON WOHLFARTH-GRILLE

1. Voy-ag-er on gold-en air, Type of all that's
2. Love-liest of all love-ly things, Ros-es o-pen
3. Van-ish'd! Earth is not___ his home; On-ward, on-ward,

fleet___ and fair, Hum-ming bird, in-car-nate gem,
to___ your wings; Hum-ming bird, each gen-tle breast,
must___ he roam; Hum-ming bird, swift pas-sion thought,

Hum-ming bird, live di - a - dem, Bird-beam of the sum - mer
Hum-ming bird, would give you rest, Stay, for - get lost par - a-
Hum-ming bird, in rap - ture wrought, Is - sue of the soul's de-

day; Whith - er on your sun - ny way?
dise; Star - bird fall'n from hap - py skies.
sire; Plumed with beau - ty and with fire.

The Traffic Man
Rote Song

ANNETTE WYNNE
Copyrighted by F. A. Stokes Company

ROSSETTER G. COLE

Moderately fast; in jolly mood

The traf-fic man stands in the square And stops the au - tos that go by.

To him a king or mil-lion-aire Is just the same as you or I.

He stops the traf - fic all the day And has the ver - y best of fun.

I think he hates to go a - way When his day's work is done.

All through the Night

Study Song

From the Welsh

DAVID OWEN

Sleep, my child, and peace at-tend thee All through the night;
While the moon her watch is keep-ing All through the night;

Guard - ian an - gels God will send thee, All through the night.
While the wea - ry world is sleep-ing All through the night,

Soft the drow-sy hours are creep-ing, Hill and vale in slum-ber steep-ing,
O'er thy spir - it gen - tly steal-ing, Vi-sions of de - light re-veal-ing,

Soft
Ah!

Tone Blending

I my lov - ing vig - il keep - ing, All through the night.
Breathes a pure and ho - ly feel - ing, All through the night.

A Song of Ripe Fruit

Study Song

NINA B. HARTFORD   NINA B. HARTFORD

"Fruit is ripe! Fruit is ripe!" Sing the or - chard trees;—"With

fruit our branch-es are lad - en, Come take as much as you please;—

Ap - ples crim - son and (ap - ples yel - low,) Peach - es jui - cy and
yel - low,

(peach - es mel - low,) Plums and grapes of dust - y blue, They're
mel - low,

all for you,—— Oh, yes, they're all for you."

My Heart's in the Highlands

Study Song

ROBERT BURNS

SCOTCH FOLK SONG

1. My heart's in the High-lands, my heart is not here; My
2. Fare - well to the High-lands, fare-well to the North, The
3. Fare - well to the moun-tains, high-cov - ered with snow; Fare-
4. My heart's in the High-lands, my heart is not here; My

heart's in the High - lands a - chas - ing the deer, A-
birth - place of val - or, the coun - try of worth; Wher-
well to the straths and green val - leys be - low; Fare-
heart's in the High - lands a - chas - ing the deer, A-

chas - ing the wild deer and fol - l'wing the roe; My
ev - er I wan - der, wher - ev - er I rove, The
well to the for - ests and wild - hang - ing woods; Fare-
chas - ing the wild deer and fol - l'wing the roe; My

heart's in the High - lands wher - ev - er I go.
hills of the High - lands for - ev - er I love.
well to the tor - rents and loud - pour - ing floods.
heart's in the High - lands wher - ev - er I go.

BEETHOVEN IN HIS STUDY, BY SCHLOESSER

A Day of Sunshine

Study Song

HENRY W. LONGFELLOW

LUDWIG VAN BEETHOVEN

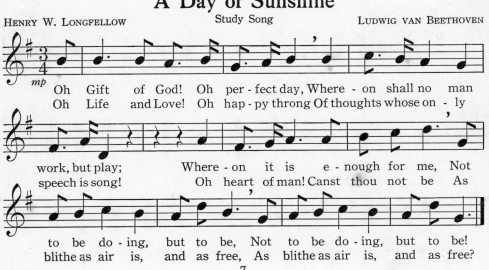

Oh Gift of God! Oh per - fect day, Where - on shall no man
Oh Life and Love! Oh hap - py throng Of thoughts whose on - ly

work, but play; Where - on it is e - nough for me, Not
speech is song! Oh heart of man! Canst thou not be As

to be do - ing, but to be, Not to be do - ing, but to be!
blithe as air is, and as free, As blithe as air is, and as free?

7

A Farewell Song

From the German   Reading Song   GERMAN FOLK SONG

1. No mat-ter where I chance to roam,   I can't for-get thee, O my home,
2. O dear-est land, land of my birth, All oth-er lands are lit-tle worth
3. Dear friends of mine, I can-not tell How hard it is   to bid fare-well
4. O home, O friends, O native land, Those who have left you un-der-stand

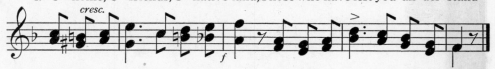

And could I choose, I would not say   Fare-well to thee, my home, to-day.
Com-pared to thee, and if   I   say   Fare-well,'tis that I must a-way.
To you who say you love me, I,   In-deed, I   can-not say good-by.
How deep my grief if I but try   To leave you, and to say good-by.

The Wayside Spring

Reading Song

LEONA UPTON   LOUIS ADOLPHE COERNE

Merrily

By a dust-y road that is steep and long, A____ way-side spring sings a

mer-ry song; Through the scorch-ing day, in the cool-ing night, It

rip-ples___on with pure de-light. From the rock-y cliff it

leaps and laughs, And its gift the thirst-y trav-'ler quaffs, And goes his way,

with a thank-ful heart For the lit-tle spring that has done its part!

An Old Legend

Reading Song

NANCY BYRD TURNER

GERMAN FOLK SONG

Andantino

1. Once a maid-en dwelt, Fair un-known,
   In a cas-tle tall, Grim gray stone. Far be-low as it flow'd a-long

2. Down the riv-er path, Ro-land came,
   Heard her plain-tive song, Call'd her__ name. Swift to-geth-er they sped a-way;

Sang the stream; she an-swered with a song, With a sad, sweet song.
Still the riv-er sings a mourn-ful lay; Sings a mourn-ful__ lay.

Tone Blending

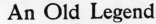

IN THE ELYSIAN FIELDS, BY BÖCKLIN

Theme
Dance of the Happy Spirits

Andante moderato

CHRISTOPH WILLIBALD VON GLUCK
from "ORPHEUS"

10

We Merry Minstrels

Three-Part Round

TRADITIONAL

HENRY PURCELL

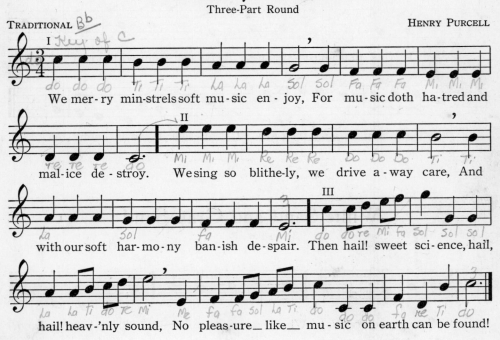

We mer-ry min-strels soft mu-sic en-joy, For mu-sic doth ha-tred and mal-ice de-stroy. We sing so blithe-ly, we drive a-way care, And with our soft har-mo-ny ban-ish de-spair. Then hail! sweet sci-ence, hail, hail! heav-'nly sound, No pleas-ure like— mu-sic on earth can be found!

Counting Ten
Rote Song

FREDERICK H. MARTENS   FRANZ JOSEPH HAYDN

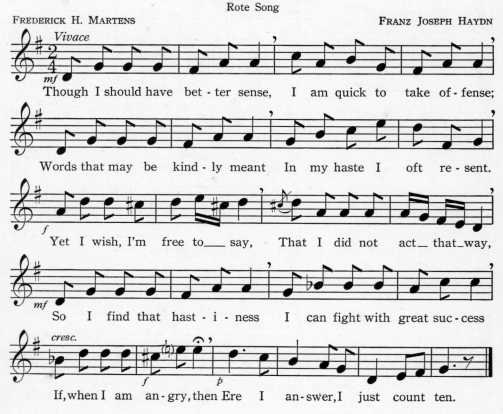

Though I should have bet-ter sense, I am quick to take of-fense;

Words that may be kind-ly meant In my haste I oft re-sent.

Yet I wish, I'm free to___ say, That I did not act___ that___way,

So I find that hast-i-ness I can fight with great suc-cess

If, when I am an-gry, then Ere I an-swer, I just count ten.

White Sand and Gray Sand
Three-Part Round

TRADITIONAL   OLD ENGLISH ROUND

White sand and gray sand, Who'll buy my white sand, Who'll buy my gray sand?

A "Movie" Dream

Reading Song

ALDIS DUNBAR

WOLFGANG AMADEUS MOZART

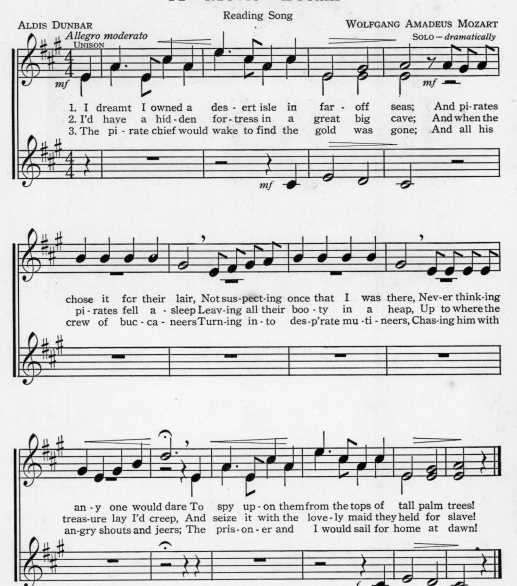

1. I dreamt I owned a des-ert isle in far-off seas; And pi-rates
2. I'd have a hid-den for-tress in a great big cave; And when the
3. The pi-rate chief would wake to find the gold was gone; And all his

chose it for their lair, Not sus-pect-ing once that I was there, Nev-er think-ing
pi-rates fell a-sleep Leav-ing all their boo-ty in a heap, Up to where the
crew of buc-ca-neers Turn-ing in-to des-p'rate mu-ti-neers, Chas-ing him with

an-y one would dare To spy up-on them from the tops of tall palm trees!
treas-ure lay I'd creep, And seize it with the love-ly maid they held for slave!
an-gry shouts and jeers; The pris-on-er and I would sail for home at dawn!

Courtesy of the Metropolitan Museum of Art

JEANNE D'ARC, BY BASTIEN-LEPAGE

Jeanne d'Arc

Reading Song

BARONESS KIEL BARNEKOW   FRENCH AIR of the XV Century

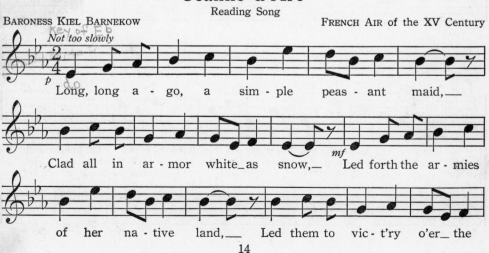

Long, long a - go, a sim - ple peas - ant maid,—

Clad all in ar - mor white as snow,— Led forth the ar - mies

of her na - tive land,— Led them to vic - t'ry o'er the

14

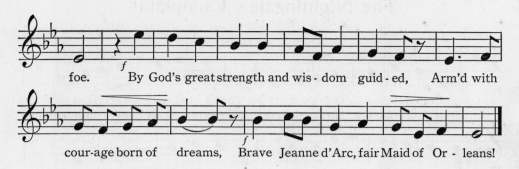

foe. By God's great strength and wis-dom guid-ed, Arm'd with

cour-age born of dreams, Brave Jeanne d'Arc, fair Maid of Or - leans!

Kelvin Grove

Reading Song

TRADITIONAL

SCOTCH FOLK SONG

Moderato

mf

Let us haste to Kel-vin grove, bon-nie las - sie, Oh; Through its
Let us wan-der by the mill,— bon-nie las - sie, Oh; To the

maz - es let us rove,— bon - nie las - sie, Oh; Where the
cove be-side the rill,— bon - nie las - sie, Oh; Where the

ros - es in their pride Deck the bon - nie din - gle side, Where the
glens re-bound the call Of the roar-ing wa-ter's fall, Through the

mid - night fair - ies glide,— bon - nie las - sie,— Oh.
moun-tain's rock - y hall,— bon - nie las - sie, Oh.

The Nightingale's Complaint
Study Song

From the original Hungarian

ANNA VON WOHLFARTH-GRILLE

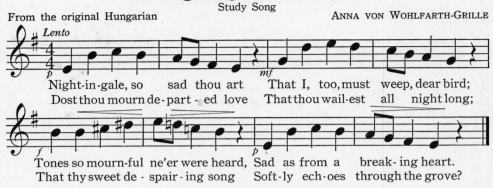

Night-in-gale, so sad thou art That I, too, must weep, dear bird;
Dost thou mourn de-part-ed love That thou wail-est all night long;

Tones so mourn-ful ne'er were heard, Sad as from a break-ing heart.
That thy sweet de-spair-ing song Soft-ly ech-oes through the grove?

Summer Has Past
Reading Song

ELIZA LEE FOLLEN

GERMAN FOLK SONG

Sweet sum-mer, with her flow'rs has past; Hear her part-ing knell! I hear the moan-ing,
I love this so-ber, sol-emn time; Twi-light of the year; To me, sweet spring, in

fit-ful blast; Sum-mer has past, List to the blast Sigh-ing a sad fare-well.
all her prime, Sweet spring-time In her prime, Was nev-er half so dear.

Tone Blending

Robin Adair
Study Song

CAROLINE KEPPEL

SCOTCH AIR

1. What's this dull town to me? Rob - in's— not— near;
   What was't I wished to see, What— wished to— hear?
   Where's all the joy and mirth That made this town a heav'n on earth?
   Oh! they're all— fled with thee, Rob - in— A - dair.

2. What made th'as - sem - bly shine? Rob - in— A - dair;
   What made the ball so fine? Rob - in— was— there.
   What, when the day was o'er, What made— my— heart so sore?
   Oh! it— was— part - ing with Rob - in— A - dair.

3. But now thou'rt far from me, Rob - in— A - dair;
   And now I nev - er see Rob - in— A - dair;
   Yet he I love so well, Still, in— my— heart shall dwell,
   Oh! I— can— ne'er for - get Rob - in— A - dair.

HENRI DE BUSSCHER PLAYING THE OBOE

Theme
From "Raymond" Overture

OBOE

AMBROISE THOMAS

Andantino ♩ = 65

Lightly

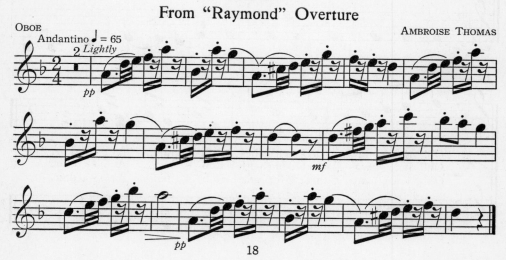

Stars of the Summer Night

Reading Song

HENRY W. LONGFELLOW

ISAAC B. WOODBURY

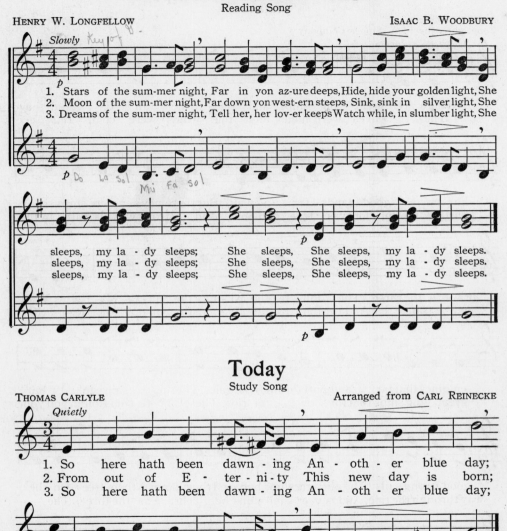

1. Stars of the sum-mer night, Far in yon az-ure deeps, Hide, hide your golden light, She
2. Moon of the sum-mer night, Far down yon west-ern steeps, Sink, sink in silver light, She
3. Dreams of the sum-mer night, Tell her, her lov-er keeps Watch while, in slumber light, She

sleeps, my la - dy sleeps; She sleeps, She sleeps, my la - dy sleeps.
sleeps, my la - dy sleeps; She sleeps, She sleeps, my la - dy sleeps.
sleeps, my la - dy sleeps; She sleeps, She sleeps, my la - dy sleeps.

Today

Study Song

THOMAS CARLYLE

Arranged from CARL REINECKE

Quietly

1. So here hath been dawn - ing An - oth - er blue day;
2. From out of E - ter - ni - ty This new day is born;
3. So here hath been dawn - ing An - oth - er blue day;

Oh, think, wilt thou let it Slip use - less a - way?
And in - to E - ter - ni - ty, At night, will re - turn.
Oh, think, wilt thou let it Slip use - less a - way?

The Three Little Ships

Rote-Song

ANNETTE WYNNE
Copyrighted by F. A. Stokes Company
DANIEL PROTHEROE

Allegretto con moto

There are great big ships and they ride all day, And they
The___ waves were mad and the winds were cold, But the

hur-ry to good_lands far a-way, But there nev-er were ships so___
heart of the pi-lot was true and bold, And___ strong was his faith in the

brave as the three, The_ Pin-ta, the Ni-na, the San-ta Ma-rie! ___ With
new_ strange sea, And the Pin-ta, the Ni-na, the San-ta Ma-rie! ___ O

en-gines that jar___ and puff through the gales, The big__ ships go; ___ but
great_ big ships that for-ev-er ride, These lit-tle ships found you your

good strong sails The lit-tle ships had, and they spread them free On the
way through the tide, And nev-er shall ships be___ brave as the three, The___

Pin-ta, the Ni-na, the San-ta Ma-rie! _____
Pin-ta, the Ni-na, the San-ta Ma-rie! _____

To the Evening Star
Study Song

ETHEL C. BROWN

ROBERT SCHUMANN

O beau-ti-ful star, So high and so far,
Your eye's search-ing light Beams down through the night.

I won-der and pon-der, So love-ly you are!
I wish I were like you, So stead-fast and bright!

Spring in Holland
Reading Song

ALDIS DUNBAR

HORTENSE, Queen of Holland

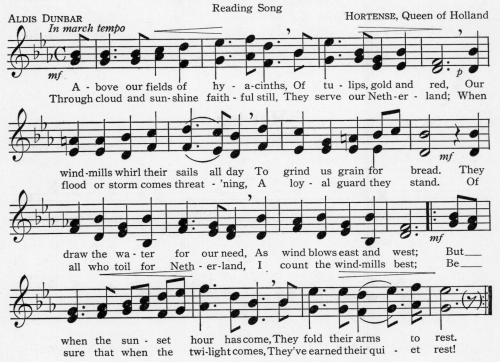

A-bove our fields of hy-a-cinths, Of tu-lips, gold and red, Our
Through cloud and sun-shine faith-ful still, They serve our Neth-er-land; When

wind-mills whirl their sails all day To grind us grain for bread. They
flood or storm comes threat-'ning, A loy-al guard they stand. Of

draw the wa-ter for our need, As wind blows east and west; But___
all who toil for Neth-er-land, I count the wind-mills best; Be___

when the sun-set hour has come, They fold their arms to rest.
sure that when the twi-light comes, They've earned their qui-et rest!

Japanese National Anthem

Study Song

English translation by
NANCY BYRD TURNER

KIMIGAYO
The National Anthem of Japan

Ki - mi ga___ yo___ wa Chi - yo ni___
May our Prince___ live to see Ten___ thou - sand___

ya - chi - yo ni Sa - za - re i - shi no I - wa - o to
years and then ten thou - sand more, Till the small peb' - bles to

na - ri - te Ko - ke no mu___ su___ ma___ de.
boul - ders grow, And these all deep___ in___ moss shall be.

Rowing

Study Song

LEONA UPTON

LOUIS ADOLPHE COERNE

With slow and swaying motion

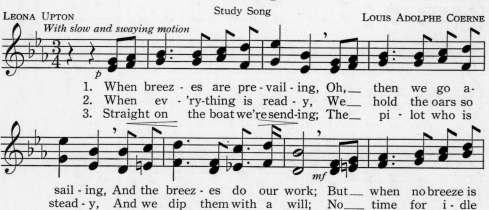

1. When breez - es are pre - vail - ing, Oh,___ then we go a -
2. When ev - 'ry-thing is read - y, We___ hold the oars so
3. Straight on the boat we're send-ing; The___ pi - lot who is

sail - ing, And the breez - es do our work; But___ when no breeze is
stead - y, And we dip them with a will; No___ time for i - dle
tend - ing To the rud - der holds it true, And___ sits and sings se -

blow - ing We___ gai - ly go a - row - ing, And there's
splash - ing, But___ just an e - ven plash - ing, That will
rene - ly, Yet___ watch - ing ev - er keen - ly O'er the

not a chance to shirk!
prove our strength and skill.
wa - ters blithe and blue, O'er the wa - ters blithe and blue.___

The Hidden Stream

Reading Song

FREDERICK H. MARTENS   JOHANN SEBASTIAN BACH

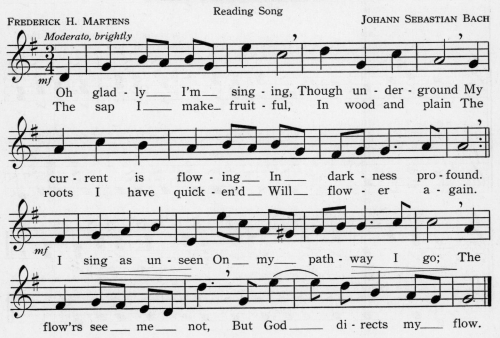

Oh glad - ly___ I'm___ sing - ing, Though un - der - ground My
The sap I___ make___ fruit - ful, In wood and plain The

cur - rent is flow - ing___ In___ dark - ness pro - found.
roots I have quick - en'd___ Will___ flow - er a - gain.

I sing as un - seen On___ my___ path - way I go; The

flow'rs see ___ me ___ not, But God___ di - rects my___ flow.

How to Tell Wild Animals

Reading Song

CAROLYN WELLS

GERMAN FOLK SONG

Mock serious

SOLO OR SEMI-CHORUS

1. If ev - er you should go by chance To jun-gles in the East; And if there should to
2. If strolling forth, a beast you view Whose hide with spots is peppered, As soon as he has
3. Though to dis-tin-guish beasts of prey A nov-ice might non-plus, The Croc - o - diles you

ritenuto

you ad-vance A large and taw-ny beast, If he roars at you as you're dyin' You'll
lept on you, You'll know it is the Leopard. 'Twill do no good to roar with pain, He'll
al-ways may Tell from Hy - e - nas thus: Hy - e - nas come with mer - ry smiles; But

CHORUS *a tempo*

know it is the As - ian Lion; If he roars at you as you're dyin' It
on - ly lep and lep a - gain; 'Twill do no good to roar with pain, He'll
if they weep, they're Croc - o - diles; Hy - e - nas come with mer - ry smiles; They

Gaily

REFRAIN

is the As - ian Lion.
lep and lep a - gain. } Li - to - ri - a! Li - to - ri - a! Swe - le - we - chu -
weep, if Croc - o - diles. }

hi - ra - sa! Li - to - ri - a! Li - to - ri - a! Swe - le - we - dum - bum!

Dawn at Carmel

Reading Song

FREDERICK H. MARTENS

CARL GROOS

On the hill of Car - mel Gold of dawn-ing__ lies,
From the mis-sion gar - dens Sweet-est o - dors__ rise;
In that morn-ing fra-grance,

Mount-ing t'ward the skies, Flow'rs of earth are greet-ing Flow'rs of par-a - dise.

Longing for the Alps

Reading Song

JAMES MONTGOMERY

ALPINE SONG

Oh,__ when shall I vis - it the land of my birth, The__ love - li - est__
When shall I re - turn to that low - ly re - treat Where all my fond__

land on the__ face__ of the earth? Oh, when shall I dance to the
ob - jects of__ ten - der - ness meet? The love - li - est land on the

sound of a reed, Be - neath a broad elm on the dai - sy__ white__ mead?
face of the earth! Oh, when shall I vis - it the land of__ my__ birth?

Courtesy of the Metropolitan Museum of Art
IN THE CONNECTICUT HILLS, BY FOSTER

Autumn Song

Reading Song

Translated by HELEN GOODRICH

FRENCH FOLK SONG

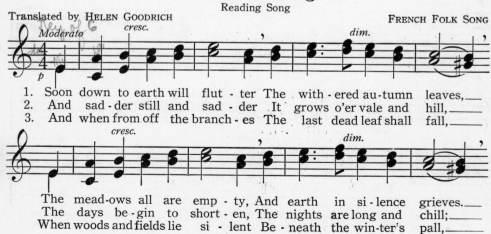

1. Soon down to earth will flut - ter The with - ered au-tumn leaves,___
2. And sad - der still and sad - der It grows o'er vale and hill,___
3. And when from off the branch - es The last dead leaf shall fall,___

The mead-ows all are emp - ty, And earth in si - lence grieves.___
The days be - gin to short - en, The nights are long and chill;___
When woods and fields lie si - lent Be - neath the win-ter's pall,___

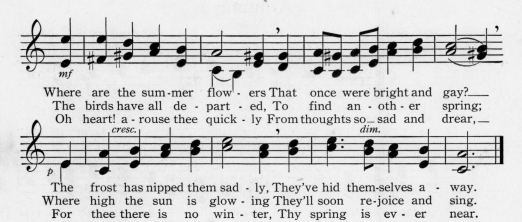

mf

Where are the sum-mer flow'-ers That once were bright and gay?——
The birds have all de-part-ed, To find an-oth-er spring;
Oh heart! a-rouse thee quick-ly From thoughts so—sad and drear,——

cresc. *dim.*

p

The frost has nipped them sad-ly, They've hid them-selves a-way.
Where high the sun is glow-ing They'll soon re-joice and sing.
For thee there is no win-ter, Thy spring is ev-er near.

To the Fringed Gentian
Reading Song

WILLIAM CULLEN BRYANT   C. A. KERN

1. Thou blos-som bright with au-tumn dew, And col-ored—with the
2. Thou com-est not when vio-lets lean O'er wan-dering brooks and
3. Thou wait-est late and com'st a-lone When woods are—bare and

heaven's own blue, That op'n-est when the qui-et light Suc-
springs un-seen, Or col-um-bines, in pur-ple dressed, Nod
birds are flown And frosts and short-'ning days por-tend The

ceeds the keen and frost-y night, Suc-ceeds the keen and frost-y night.
o'er the ground-bird's hid-den nest, Nod o'er the groundbird's hid-den nest.
a-ged year is near the end, The a-ged year is near the end.

Autumn
Reading Song

FREDERICK MANLEY

Arranged by C. GRAMM

Moderato

1. If ev - er in a shad - y hol - low, When sum - mer
2. Step qui - et - ly in - to the bush - es, And if you
3. A gen - 'rous pip - er for his blow - ing Loads all the
4. Should you be fast e - nough to fol - low As he goes

day - light short - er grows, You come a - cross a jol - ly fel - low With
watch you'll see him make A flag - eo - let of riv - er rush - es Where-
barns with yel - low sheaves, And tells the birds they must be go - ing To
pip - ing mer - ri - ly, You'll see him blow, the kind - ly fel - low, Rich

gold - en leaves a - bout his brows, And gar - ment - ed in rus - set clothes,
on he blows till wood - lands wake, And of its joc - und notes par - take.
south - ern lands where sun - ny eaves Are ly - ing 'mongst the sum - mer leaves.
fruits a - bout the fields and leas, And ap - ples from the or - chard trees.

O'er the Steppes
Reading Song

NANCY BYRD TURNER

RUSSIAN FOLK SONG

Dim for - bid - ding and still Spread the steppes, cold and wan.
O'er the des - o - late wastes On - ward lone - ly they roam,

Horse and rid - er plod slow - ly, On, for - ev - er on.
Soft and sad - ly the horse - man Hums a song___ of home.

God Speed the Right

Reading Song

W. E. HICKSON

GERMAN FOLK SONG

1. Now to heav'n our prayer as-cend-ing, God speed the right;
   In our no - ble cause con-tend-ing, God speed the right;
2. Be that prayer a - gain re-peat-ed, God speed the right;
   Ne'er de-spair-ing, though de-feat-ed; God speed the right;
3. Still our on - ward course pur-su - ing, God speed the right;
   Ev - 'ry foe at length sub-du-ing, God speed the right;

Be our zeal in heav'n re-cord-ed; With suc-cess on earth re-
Like the good and great in sto-ry, If we fail, we fail in
Truth our cause, what-e'er de - lay it, There's no power on earth to

ward - ed. God speed the right, God speed the right.
glo - ry, God speed the right, God speed the right.
stay it, God speed the right, God speed the right.

Tone Blending

Twilight Song

Reading Song

FLEUR CONKLING

ITALIAN FOLK SONG

Night now draws nigh, Stars fill the sky,
Soft - ly the wind, Mur - murs its song,

Fair gleams the sil - ver moon on high.
Rock - ing the tree tops all night long.

Deep in the tall trees, Safe from the chill breeze,
Wee birds are sleep - ing, Moon - beams are keep - ing

Birds seek their nest; The world is___ at rest.
Watch o'er the nest; The world is___ at rest.

Deep in___ the tall trees, Safe from___ the chill breeze,
Wee birds___ are sleep - ing, Moon - beams___ are keep - ing

Birds seek their nest; The world is___ at rest.
Watch o'er the nest; The world is___ at rest.

Wioste Olowan
Study Song

From "THE INDIANS' BOOK" by
NATALIE CURTIS, published by
HARPER & BROTHERS

(LOVE SONG) DAKOTA TRIBE

Ink-pa - ta ya na-wa zin Na___ si - na ci co ze - e
Up the creek I stand and wave; See,___ all a - lone I wave!___

Ma - ya___ Ma - ya,___ Le ciya Ku - wan - na!___
Ah, hith - er, Ah, hith - er Haste___ thee to me!___

Lullaby
Reading Song

Translated from the German

FERDINAND HILLER

Andante dolce

1. Sleep - y winds sigh far___ and near.___ Lit - tle chil - dren,
2. Sleep - y winds sigh far___ and near.___ Lit - tle trees their
3. Sleep - y winds sigh far___ and near.___ E - ven jol - ly

tired___ of play - ing, Now their eve - ning prayers are say - ing;
heads are nod - ding, Tired of grow - ing, tired___ of bud - ding;
fire___ is nap - ping, Soft gray blan - kets round___him wrap - ping;

Then they sleep, ___ my ba - by dear, ___ my ba - by dear.___
So___ they sleep, ___ my ba - by dear, ___ my ba - by dear.___
Soon he'll sleep; ___ like ba - by dear, ___ like ba - by dear.___

Auld Lang Syne

Reading Song

ROBERT BURNS   SCOTCH AIR

Should auld ac-quaint-ance be for-got, And nev-er brought to mind?
And here's a hand, my trust-y frien' And gie's a hand o' thine,

Should auld ac-quaint-ance be for-got, And days of auld lang syne?
We'll tak' a cup o' kind-ness yet, For auld___ lang___ syne.

For auld___ lang___ syne, my dear, For auld___ lang___ syne;

We'll tak' a cup o' kind-ness yet, For auld___ lang___ syne.

Tone Blending

Harvest Home
Reading Song

JOHN DRYDEN

HENRY. PURCELL

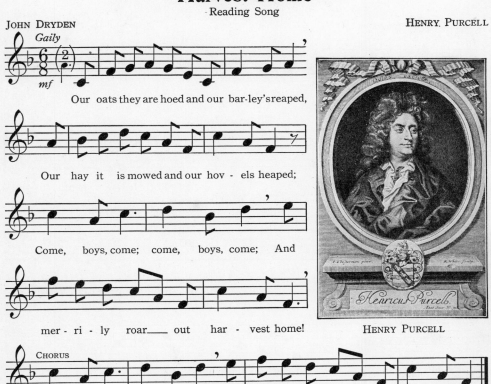

Gaily

mf

Our oats they are hoed and our bar-ley's reaped,

Our hay it is mowed and our hov-els heaped;

Come, boys, come; come, boys, come; And

mer-ri-ly roar___ out har-vest home!

CHORUS

f

Har-vest home! Har-vest home! We'll mer-ri-ly roar___ out har-vest home!

HENRY PURCELL

Morning Papers
Three-Part Round

TRADITIONAL

OLD ENGLISH ROUND

I

II

III

Morn-ing pa-pers, morn-ing pa-pers, all the ri-ots, rows, and capers; "Times," "Daily News."

Leaves at Play

Rote Song - School Choir

Frank Dempster Sherman

W. Otto Miessner

Merrily

1. Scam-per, lit-tle leaves, a-bout In the au-tumn sun; I can
2. When you've run a month or so Ver-y tired you'll get; But the
3. Run on and have your play, Romp with all your might; Dance a-

1. Scam-per, lit-tle leaves, a-bout In the
2. When you've run a month or so Ver-y
3. Run on and have your play, Romp with

hear the old Wind shout, Laugh-ing as you run, And I
same old Wind, I know, Will be laugh - ing yet, When he
cross the au-tumn day, While the sun is bright; Soon you'll

au - tumn sun; I can hear him laugh - ing as you run
tired you'll get; But the old Wind will be laugh-ing yet.
all your might; Danc-ing gai-ly while the sun is bright;

have - n't an - y doubt That he likes the fun.
tucks you deep in snow, Down-y cov - er - let.
hear the old Wind say, "Lit-tle leaves, Good-night!"

And I have - n't an - y doubt That he likes the fun.
When he tucks you deep in snow, Down-y cov-er-let.
I can hear the old Wind say, "Lit-tle leaves, Good-night!"

Golden Slumbers

Reading Song

TRADITIONAL

ENGLISH FOLK TUNE

Gold - en slum-bers kiss your eyes, Smiles a - wake you when you rise.
Care you know not, there-fore sleep While o'er you safe watch I keep.

Sleep, pret-ty dar - ling, do___ not cry, And I will sing a lull-a - by.
Sleep, pret-ty dar - ling, do___ not cry, And I will sing a lull-a - by.

lull - a - by.___

Lull-a - by, lull-a - by, lull - a - by.___
Lull-a - by, lull-a - by, lull - a - by.___

The Snow

Study Song - School Choir

ALICE V. L. CARRICK

MAX REGER

Con moto

Last night__ the__ hills were brown__ and bare, The__
Each hill - top__ has a gleam - ing crown, And__

trees__ had not a leaf__ to__ wear, But now the whole wide
ev - 'ry tree a span - gled_ gown! I won - der who came

sky__ is blue, And all the world seems made__ a - new.
down_ last night, And dressed the world in blue__ and white?

The Last Rose of Summer

Study Song

THOMAS MOORE

IRISH FOLK SONG, version by SIR CHARLES V. STANFORD.
(For other versions see Teacher's Guide for the Fifth Book)

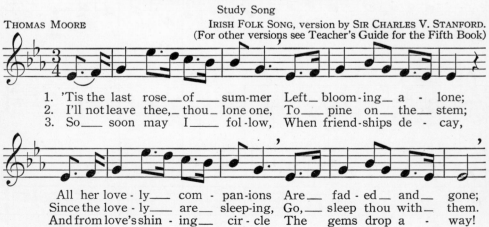

1. 'Tis the last rose__ of__ sum-mer Left__ bloom-ing__ a - lone;
2. I'll not leave thee,__ thou_ lone one, To__ pine on__ the__ stem;
3. So__ soon may I__ fol-low, When friend-ships de - cay,

All her love - ly__ com - pan-ions Are__ fad - ed__ and__ gone;
Since the love - ly__ are_ sleep-ing, Go,__ sleep thou with__ them.
And from love's shin - ing__ cir - cle The gems drop a - way!

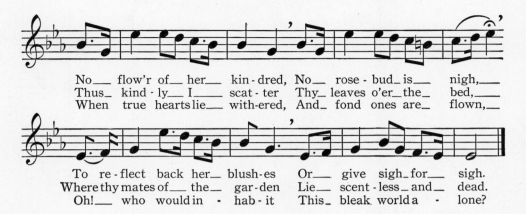

No__ flow'r of__ her__ kin-dred, No__ rose-bud_ is__ nigh,__
Thus_ kind-ly__ I__ scat-ter Thy_ leaves o'er__the_ bed,__
When true hearts lie__ with-ered, And_ fond ones are_ flown,__

To re-flect back her__ blush-es Or__ give sigh_for__ sigh.
Where thy mates of__ the__ gar-den Lie__ scent-less_ and__ dead.
Oh!__ who would in-hab-it This_ bleak world a-lone?

Weel May the Keel Row

Reading Song

TRADITIONAL   SCOTCH HIGHLAND FOLK SONG

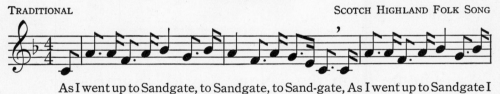

As I went up to Sandgate, to Sandgate, to Sand-gate, As I went up to Sandgate I

heard a las-sie sing, Oh weel may the keel row, the keel row, the keel row, Oh

weel may the keel row That my_ lad-die's in.   Weel may the keel row, the

keel row, the keel_row, Weel may the keel row That my_ lad-die's in.

Kubey-Rembrandt Studios, Phila.

JOSEPH WOLFE PLAYING THE ENGLISH HORN

Theme from the "New World" Symphony

ENGLISH HORN

ANTONIN DVOŘÁK

Let Songs of Praise Arise
Reading Song

GEORGE ROGERS

JOHANN SEBASTIAN BACH

1. Let songs of praise a - rise To God at ear - ly morn,
2. At noon - tide, too, O Lord, Thy praise shall be our theme,
3. At eve - ning's star - lit hour, Still be His praise ex - pressed,

When gold - en beams from east - ern skies The moun - tain peaks a - dorn.
When floods of burn - ing light are poured O'er moun - tain, vale, and stream.
When count - less stars of light His power And watch - ful love at - test.

Let Us with a Gladsome Mind
Study Song

JOHN MILTON

OLD TUNE

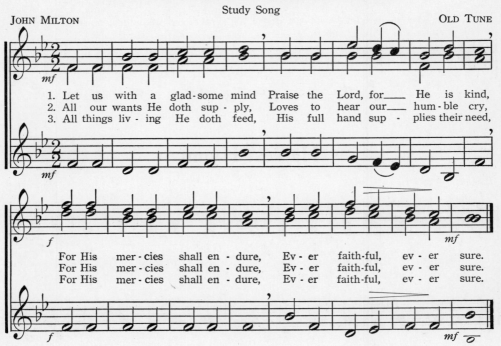

1. Let us with a glad - some mind Praise the Lord, for___ He is kind,
2. All our wants He doth sup - ply, Loves to hear our___ hum - ble cry,
3. All things liv - ing He doth feed, His full hand sup - plies their need,

For His mer - cies shall en - dure, Ev - er faith - ful, ev - er sure.
For His mer - cies shall en - dure, Ev - er faith - ful, ev - er sure.
For His mer - cies shall en - dure, Ev - er faith - ful, ev - er sure.

The Pilgrim Fathers

Reading Song

LEONARD BACON

LOWELL MASON

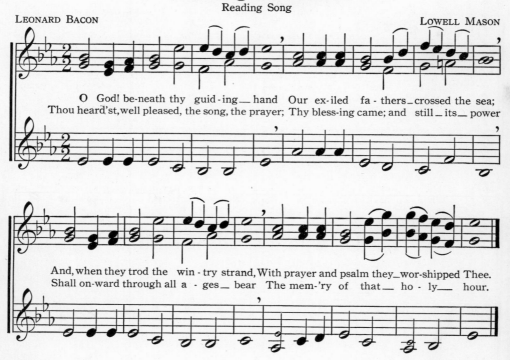

O God! be-neath thy guid-ing — hand Our ex-iled fa-thers — crossed the sea;
Thou heard'st, well pleased, the song, the prayer; Thy bless-ing came; and still — its — power

And, when they trod the win-try strand, With prayer and psalm they — wor-shipped Thee.
Shall on-ward through all a-ges — bear The mem-'ry of that — ho-ly — hour.

Harvest Hymn

Reading Song

HENRY ALFORD

G. J. ELVEY

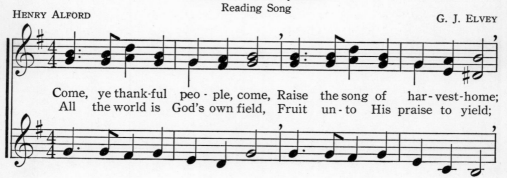

Come, ye thank-ful peo-ple, come, Raise the song of har-vest-home;
All the world is God's own field, Fruit un-to His praise to yield;

All is safe-ly gath-ered in   Ere the win-ter storms be-gin
Wheat and tares to-geth-er sown,   Un-to joy or sor-row grown

God, our Mak-er, doth pro-vide   For our wants to be sup-plied;
First the blade, and then the ear,   Then the full corn shall ap-pear;

Come to God's own tem-ple, come, Raise the song of har-vest-home.
Lord of har-vest, grant that we Whole-some grain and pure may be.

Tone Blending

Planting Hops

Reading Song

From the Russian,
by NATHAN HASKELL DOLE

ALEXANDER GRETCHANINOFF

ALEXANDER GRETCHANINOFF

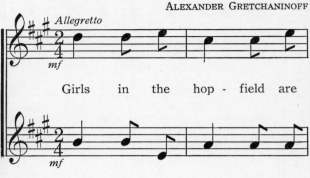

Girls in the hop - field are

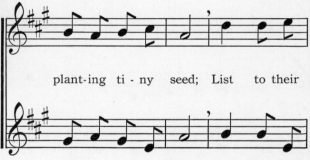

plant-ing ti - ny seed; List to their

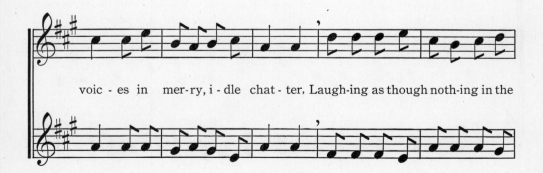

voic - es in mer-ry, i - dle chat - ter, Laugh-ing as though noth-ing in the

world could ev-er mat-ter; Sound advice and counsel wise they never, never heed!

Grow, seed, grow, climb the lat - tice high; Grow, lit-tle seed, just as

we— are grow - ing Ev-'ry day a lit-tle more of do - ing and

Ev-'ry day more do - ing,

know - ing; Thus our hap-py lives may flow-er by_ and by!

know - ing; Thus our

Santa Lucia

Study Song

TRADITIONAL

ITALIAN FOLK SONG

Andantino

1. Now 'neath the sil-ver moon O-cean is glow-ing, O'er the calm bil - low
Here balm-y zeph-yrs blow, Pure joys in-vite us, And as we gen-tly row

2. When o'er thy wa - ters Light winds are play-ing, Thy spell can soothe_ us,
To thee, sweet Na-po-li, What charms are giv-en, Where smiles cre-a - tion,

Soft winds are blow-ing,
All things de-light us. { Hark, how the sail-or's cry Joy-ous-ly ech-oes nigh.
All care al - lay-ing. { Home of fair po-e-sy, Realm of pure Har-mo-ny,
Toil blest by heav-en.

San-ta_Lu - ci - a! San-ta Lu-ci - a,
San-ta_Lu - ci - a! San-ta Lu-ci - a!

The Rose-Tree
Study Song

English version by
ABBIE FARWELL BROWN

MICHAEL PRAETORIUS

win-ter's frost___ and cold.
joy for young___ and old.
shel-ter 'neath___ the Tree.
glow-ing mys - ter - y.

1. There is a Rose-Tree bloom - ing In win-ter's frost___ and cold;
   To tell how Spring is com - ing, With joy for young___ and old.
2. Lo, an - y life that shiv - ers May shel-ter 'neath___ the Tree.
   Each ten-der pet - al quiv - ers, With glow-ing mys - ter - y.

It is the Rose of Love,___ No cru - el
And 'mid the sweet - ness curled___ A gold - en

tem - pest can___ re - move.
treas - ure of___ the world!

wind can with - er, No tem-pest can re - move.
heart is hid - den, Dear treas-ure of the___ world!

198 T.M.

198

Italian Street Fair

Rote Song *198*

FLEUR CONKLING

ITALIAN FOLK SONG

Alla marcia

At the street fair____

Courtesy of the Metropolitan Museum of Art

ROMAN GIRL AT A FOUNTAIN, BY BONNAT

We mer - ri - ly dance to - day,____

To mu - sic that's bright and gay,____

And ped - dle our wares; Come and buy!

Gold - en oran - ges____ and clus - ters of

grapes are seen,____ So lus - cious in leaves of green;____ Come buy at the fair! Dance

man with the hand or - gan's

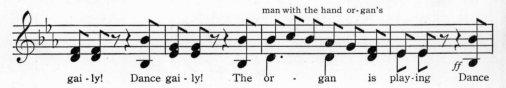

gai - ly! Dance gai - ly! The or - gan is play - ing Dance

gai - ly   Dance gai - ly!   Come dance at the fair!   Ho!

Christmas Carol
Study Song

ALDIS DUNBAR

OLD FRENCH CAROL

lit - tle King of Love!
lit - tle sleep-ing One!

Why shines one star so clear to - night? Sleep, sleep, King of Love!
See, all ye An - gels, bend-ing near, Hush Thee, sleep-ing One!

strong and pure and bright,
sleep-eth sweet-ly here,

By its glo-rious light, strong, pure, bright, Seraphs wing their way to earth from
He whom ye re - vere, sleep - eth here, In a man-ger low, His life on

a-
be-
seek - ing One they love.
sleep, Thou love - ly One!

heav'n a - bove. Seek - ing, One they love.
earth be - gun. Sleep, Thou, love - ly One!

Home, Sweet Home

Reading Song

JOHN HOWARD PAYNE

HENRY R. BISHOP

Moderato

mf

'Mid— pleas - ures and pal - ac - es though we may roam, Be it
An— ex - ile from home, splen-dor daz - zles in vain, Oh,—

ev - er so hum-ble, there's no— place like home! A charm from the
give— me my low-ly thatched cot - tage a - gain! The birds— sing-ing

skies seems to hal - low us there, Which, seek through the world, is ne'er
gai - ly 'that come— at my call; Give me them— with the peace of mind,

REFRAIN

p   mf

met— with else-where.   Home! home!— sweet, sweet home! There's
dear - er than all.

p   mf

no— place like home,— there's no— place like home.

Sea Horses
Study Song

HAMISH HENRY   ELEANOR SMITH

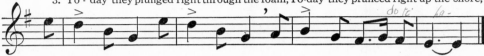

1. I saw them plung-ing through the foam, I saw them pac - ing up the shore,
2. In fear they leapt_up - on the land, In fear they fled__ be - fore the wind,
3. To - day they plunged right through the foam, To-day they pranced right up the shore,

A thou - sand hors - es, row on row, And then a thou - sand more.__
And, pranc - ing, plung - ing, on they raced The hunts - man raced be - hind.__
A thou - sand hors - es, row on row, And then a thou - sand more.__

Now the Day Is Over
Reading Song

SABINE BARING-GOULD   JOSEPH BARNBY

1. Now the day is__ o - ver, Night is draw-ing__ nigh,__
2. Now the dark - ness_ gath - ers,__ Stars be - gin to__ peep,__
3. When the morn - ing_ wak - ens,__ Then may I a - rise__

Shad - ows of the eve - ning__ Steal a - cross the sky.
Birds and beasts and flow - ers,__ Soon will be a - sleep.
Pure and fresh and sin - less__ In Thy ho - ly eyes.

The King of China's Daughter

Rote Song - School Choir

EDITH SITWELL

MABEL W. DANIELS

Gaily and lightly

The King of Chi - na's daugh - ter So beau - ti - ful to

see With her face like yel - low wa - ter, Left her nut - meg

tree. Her lit - tle rope for skip - ping,   for

Her lit - tle rope for skip - ping, for

skip - ping She skipped,   she skipped,   she skipped and gave it

Smoothly, dolce

me,   Made of paint - ed notes of sing - ing birds, A-

mong the fields of tea._____ I

skipped a-cross the nut-meg grove, I skipped a-cross the sea; _____ But

I skipped a-cross But

neith - er sun nor moon, my dear, Has yet caught me.

Good Night

Reading Song

ELSIE COBB BARNARD   WILLIAM G. HAMMOND

1. The lit - tle new moon's cra - dle bow A - down the west is
2. The dew is glis - t'ning on the grass; It marks the steps of
3. The flow - ers sleep and dream a - gain Of shin - ing sun and

rock - ing low. The last faint rays of sun - set light Are
those who pass. The south - wind lin - gers in her flight, And
cool - ing rain. The but - ter - fly now stills its flight, All

shin - ing forth, "Good night, good night." _____
soft - ly sighs, "Good night, good night." _____
na - ture sleeps, "Good night, good night." _____

Carol of the Shepherds

Reading Song

EDA LOU WALTON

BOHEMIAN FOLK SONG

Moderato

1. Come, all__ ye__ shep-herds and__ be not__ dis-mayed, Seek where the__
2. As we__were watch-ing__ our flocks where they lay, Shone a__ great__
3. Now we__have found Him__ in Beth-le-hem__ stall, Sing the__ glad__

1. Come, ye shep-herds, un - dis-mayed; Where the
2. We were watch - ing where they lay, Shone a
3. We have found Him in a stall, Sing glad

low - ly__ sweet__ ba - by__ is__ laid; Here in a man-ger,
glo - ry__ as__ bright as__ the__ day. Glad bells were ring-ing,
tid - ings,__ oh__ sing them__ to__ all! Shep - herds a - dore Him,

low - ly babe is laid;
glo - ry bright as day.
tid - ings, sing to all!

far from all dan-ger, Sleep-ing be-hold Him, warm arms en-fold Him In Christ-mas joy.
sweet voices singing, Through heav'n's blue portals, "Good will to mortals;" Christ-mas is come.
wise men be-fore Him Lay down their dow-er, in glit-t'ring show-er, Christ-mas is come.

Theme
From "Symphony Pathétique"

CLARINET *Andante (con tenerezza)*

PETER ILICH TSCHAIKOWSKY

PETER ILICH TSCHAIKOWSKY

Christmas Stars
Study Song

FREDERICK H. MARTENS

RUSSIAN FOLK SONG, used by TSCHAIKOWSKY as the theme in the "ANDANTE CANTABILE" of the String Quartet, op. 11.

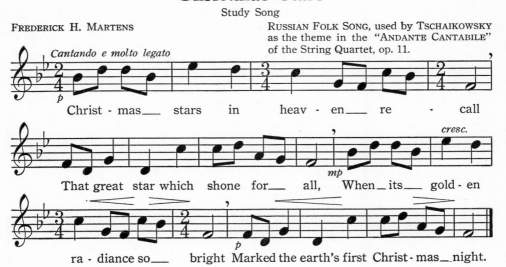

Cantando e molto legato

Christ - mas___ stars in heav - en___ re - call

That great star which shone for___ all, When___ its___ gold - en

ra - diance so___ bright Marked the earth's first Christ - mas___ night.

The Plaint of the Camel

Study Song - School Choir

CHARLES EDWARD CARRYL   MARSHALL BARTHOLOMEW

Slowly, grudgingly

1. Ca - na - ry birds feed ____ on sug - ar and seed, ____ The
2. Cats, you're a - ware, can re - pose in a chair, ____
3. Lambs are en - closed where it's nev - er ex - posed, ____
4. Peo - ple would laugh if you rode a gi - raffe, ____ Or
5. A snake is as round as a hole in the ground, And

par - rots have crack-ers to crunch, And as for the poo-dles, they
Chick-ens can roost up - on nails; Pup-pies are a - ble to
Coops are con-struc-ted for hens; Kit-tens are treat-ed to
mount-ed the back of an ox; It's no-bod-y's hab - it to
wea-sels are wav - y and sleek; And no al - li - ga - tor could

tell me the noo - dles Have chick - ens and cream for their lunch.
sleep in a sta - ble, And oys - ters can slum - ber in pails.
hous - es well heat - ed, And pigs are pro - tec - ted by pens.
ride on a rab - bit, Or try to be - strad - dle a fox.
ev - er be straight - er Than liz - ards that live in a creek.

poco rit.

But there's nev - er a ques - tion A - bout my di - ges - tion ____
But ____ no one sup - pos - es A poor cam - el doz - es ____
But a cam - el comes hand - y Wher - ev - er it's sand - y ____
But ____ as for a cam - el, He's rid - den by fam - i - lies
But a cam - el's all lump - y And bump - y and hump - y ____

a tempo

An - y-thing does for me, ____ An - y-thing does for me!____
An - y place does for me, ____ An - y place does for me!____
An - y-where does for me, ____ An - y-where does for me!____
An - y load does for me, ____ An - y load does for me!____
An - y shape does for me, ____ An - y shape does for me!____

Come, Thou Almighty King

Reading Song

CHARLES WESLEY

FELICE DE GIARDINI

Come, Thou Al - might - y King, Help us Thy name— to sing,
Come, Thou in - car - nate word, Gird on Thy might - y sword,

Help us to praise. Fa - ther all glo - ri - ous, O'er all vic -
Our pray'r at - tend. Come, and Thy peo - ple bless, And give Thy

to - ri - ous, Come and reign o - ver us, An - cient of days.
word suc - cess, Spir - it of ho - li - ness, On us de - scend.

Tone Blending

Evening Song

Reading Song

From "CHAMBERS' JOURNAL"

ROBERT SCHUMANN

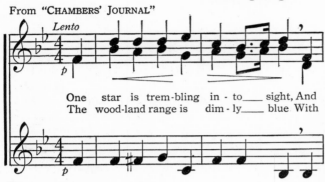

ROBERT SCHUMANN

One star is trem-bling in-to___ sight, And
The wood-land range is dim-ly___ blue With

soft as sleep the dark-ness___ falls, The
smoke, that creeps from cots un-seen, And

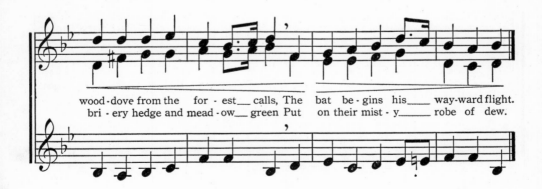

wood-dove from the for-est___ calls, The bat be-gins his___ way-ward flight.
bri-ery hedge and mead-ow___ green Put on their mist-y___ robe of dew.

Amaryllis

Reading Song

EDA LOU WALTON

HENRI GHYS

Daintily

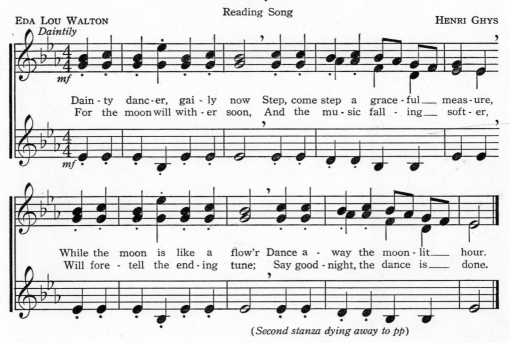

Dain - ty danc-er, gai - ly now Step, come step a grace-ful__ meas-ure,
For the moon will with-er soon, And the mu-sic fall - ing__ soft-er,

While the moon is like a flow'r Dance a - way the moon-lit__ hour.
Will fore - tell the end-ing tune; Say good-night, the dance is__ done.

(Second stanza dying away to pp)

Peaceful Night

Reading Song

FLEUR CONKLING

LUDWIG VAN BEETHOVEN

Slowly, with much expression

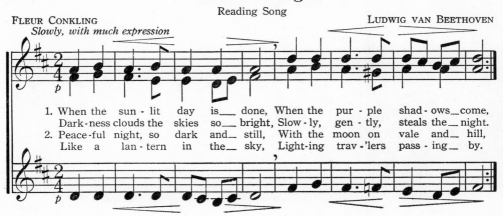

1. When the sun - lit day is__ done, When the pur - ple shad - ows__ come,
   Dark - ness clouds the skies so__ bright, Slow - ly, gen - tly, steals the__ night.
2. Peace - ful night, so dark and__ still, With the moon on vale and__ hill,
   Like a lan - tern in the__ sky, Light-ing trav - 'lers pass - ing__ by.

CHRISTMAS EVE IN MERRY ENGLAND, BY SHIRLEY KITE

The Waits

Reading Song

A. J. FOXWELL

JEREMIAH SAVILLE

When the Christ - mas time is at hand, Then the waits are
When the dark - ness hides them from sight, We can hear them
Fa la la la la la la la, Fa la la la

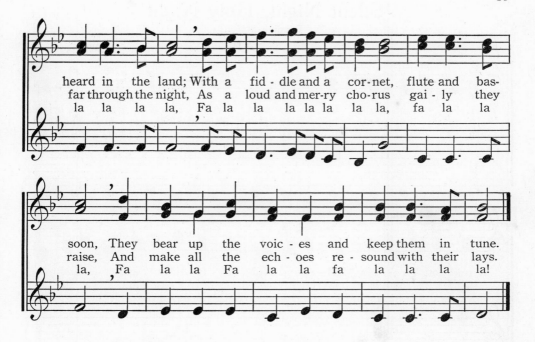

heard in the land; With a fid - dle and a cor-net, flute and bas-
far through the night, As a loud and mer-ry cho-rus gai - ly they
la la la la, Fa la la la la la la la, fa la la

soon, They bear up the voic - es and keep them in tune.
raise, And make all the ech - oes re - sound with their lays.
la, Fa la la Fa la la fa la la la la!

Waltz in A-flat

Theme

JOHANNES BRAHMS

Slow Waltz
dolce

Silent Night, Holy Night

Reading Song

JOSEPH MOHR   FRANZ GRUBER

1. Si - lent night, ho - ly night, All is calm, all is bright
2. Si - lent night, ho - ly night, Shep-herds quake at the sight,
3. Si - lent night, ho - ly night, Son of God, love's pure light

Round yon Vir - gin Moth - er and Child, Ho - ly In-fant so ten-der and mild,
Glo - ries stream from heav-en a - far, Heav-'nly hosts sing, "Al - le - lu - ia;
Ra - diant beams from Thy ho - ly face, With the dawn of re-deem-ing grace,

Sleep in heav-en-ly peace,___ Sleep in heav-en-ly peace.___
Christ, the Sav-iour is born!___ Christ, the Sav-iour is born!"___
Je - sus, Lord, at Thy birth,___ Je - sus, Lord, at Thy birth!___

Tone Blending

Market Day
Study Song

ETHEL C. BROWN

ROBERT SCHUMANN

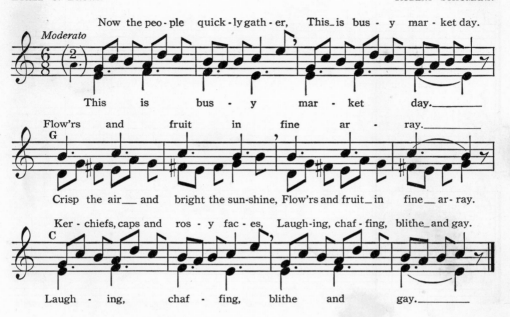

Now the peo - ple quick - ly gath - er, This is bus - y mar - ket day.

This is bus - y mar - ket day._____

Flow'rs and fruit in fine ar - ray._____

Crisp the air__ and bright the sun-shine, Flow'rs and fruit__ in fine ar - ray.

Ker - chiefs, caps and ros - y fac - es, Laugh-ing, chaf - fing, blithe__ and gay.

Laugh - ing, chaf - fing, blithe and gay._____

Winter Landscape
Reading Song

MARY J. M. LARKIN

CARL MARIA VON WEBER

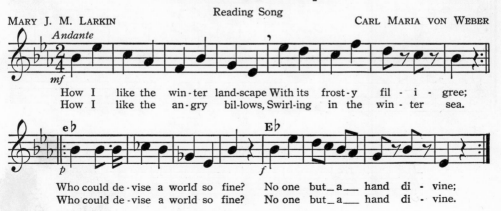

How I like the win - ter land-scape With its frost-y fil - i - gree;
How I like the an - gry bil-lows, Swirl-ing in the win - ter sea.

Who could de - vise a world so fine? No one but a__ hand di - vine;
Who could de - vise a world so fine? No one but a__ hand di - vine.

Happy New Year

Study Song - School Choir

Isabel M. Higdon

Isabel M. Higdon

Ring out the old,— Ring in the New Year, "Hap-py New Year, Hap-py New Year!"

It is the time— of joy and glad-ness and of good cheer, "Hap-py New Year!"

It is the hour— of new res-o- lu-tions, We hope to keep (to keep) through-out the

Tone Blending

year.— To all we meet— the joy-ous greet-ings, "Hap-py New Year, Hap-py New Year!"

New Year's Hymn
Reading Song

FRANCES RIDLEY HAVERGAL

EDWARD BAILEY BIRGE

Allegro moderato

mf

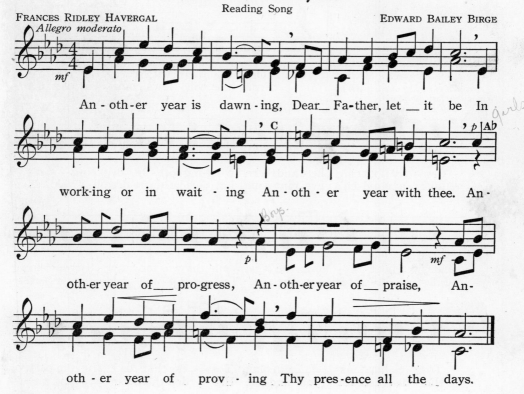

An - oth-er year is dawn-ing, Dear— Fa-ther, let — it be In

work-ing or in wait - ing An - oth - er year with thee. An -

oth-er year of— pro-gress, An - oth-er year of— praise, An-

oth - er year of prov - ing Thy pres -ence all the days.

A Boating Song

Reading Song

REBECCA B. FORESMAN

WOLFGANG AMADEUS MOZART

Key of Eb

Allegretto dolce

WOLFGANG AMADEUS MOZART

From a painting made when he was fourteen years old.

With the love-ly moon a-bove us
There is noth-ing to af-fright us

We___ are glid-ing free___ from care
As___ we calm-ly glide___ a-long;

On the stream with scarce a rip-ple,
From the wil-lows comes a whis-per

Gen-tly float-ing here and there. Swing-ing soft-ly, drift-ing i-dly,
Like a maid-en's eve-ning song. Let us heed no dream-y voic-es

Glides our boat a-long___ the way, While the wa-ter, gen-tly swell-ing,
Call-ing on-ward to___ the sea, Tell-ing of the gold-en treas-ures

Toss-es her___ as if___ in play, Toss-es her___ as if___ in play.
Hid-den there for you and me, Hid-den there for you and me.

God, Our Maker

MRS. C. F. ALEXANDER

Reading Song

WILLIAM HENRY MONK
Arranged by RUSSELL CARTER

1. All things bright and beau-ti-ful, All crea-tures great and small,

All things wise and won-der-ful, The Lord God made them all.

2. Each lit-tle flow'r that o-pens, Each lit-tle bird that sings,
3. The pur-ple-head-ed moun-tain, The riv-er run-ning by,
4. The cold wind in the win-ter, The pleas-ant sum-mer sun,
5. He gave us eyes to see them, And lips that we might tell

He made their flow-ing col-ors, He made their ti-ny wings.
The sun-set and the morn-ing That bright-ens up the sky.
The ripe fruits in the gar-den, He made them ev-'ry one.
How great is God Al-might-y, Who has made all things well.

The Kine Are Homeward Going

Three-Part Round

TRADITIONAL

OLD ENGLISH ROUND

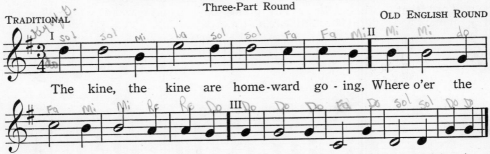

The kine, the kine are home-ward go-ing, Where o'er the

ford the stream is flow-ing, They drink and wan-der on-ward, low-ing.

Morning Hymn

Reading Song

J. KEBLE

LUDWIG VAN BEETHOVEN

1. Lord God of morn - ing and__ of night, We thank Thee
2. Fresh hopes have wak - ened in__ the heart, Fresh force to
3. O Lord of light, 'tis Thou__ a - lone Canst make our
4. Praise God, our Mak - er and__ our Friend; Praise Him through

for Thy gifts__ of light; As in the dawn__ the
do our dai - ly part; Thy slum - ber gifts__ our
dark - ened hearts__ thine own; Oh then be with__ us,
time, till time__ shall end; Till psalm and song__ His

shad - ows fly,__ We seem to find__ Thee now__ more nigh.
strength re - store, Through-out the day__ to serve__ Thee more.
Lord, that we__ In Thy great day__ may wake__ to Thee.
name a - dore Through heav'n's great day of ev - er - more.

Tone Blending

O Light-Bearing Star

Reading Song

A. J. FOXWELL   C. H. FISCHER

Andantino

1. O___ light-bear-ing star,   Thou rid-est___ a-
2. Thy___ glanc-es___ of fire   My heart will___ in-
3. Like___ thee, be___ it mine   Un-cloud-ed___ to___

1. O   light-bear-ing___ star,   Thou___
2. Thy   glanc-es___ of___ fire   My___
3. Like   thee, be___ it___ mine   Un-

far,   Re-splend-ent in___ beau-ty, A___ Queen in   thy
spire   With___ fond as-pi-ra-tion To___ gaze and ad-
shine,   And___ gain for my___ guer-don Ap-prov-al di-

rid-est___ a-far,   Re-splend-ent in   beau-ty,___ A___
heart will___ in-spire   With fond as-pi-ra-tion___ To___
cloud-ed___ to shine,   And gain for my   guer-don Ap-

car,   Re-splend-ent in___ beau-ty,___ A Queen   in thy car.
mire,   With fond as-pi-ra-tion To gaze   and ad-mire.
vine,   And___gain for___ my guer-don Ap-prov-al di-vine.

Queen in thy   car,   A Queen,___ A   Queen in thy car.
gaze and ad-mire,   To gaze,___ To   gaze_and ad-mire.
prov-al di-vine,   Ap-prov-al, Ap-   prov-al di-vine.

Thanksgiving Hymn

Reading Song

ANONYMOUS

NETHERLANDS TUNE

Lento

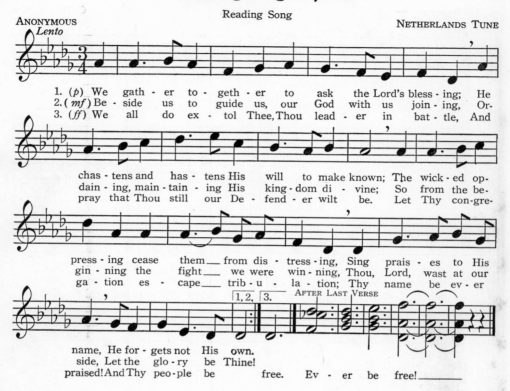

1. (p) We gath-er to-geth-er to ask the Lord's bless-ing; He
2. (mf) Be-side us to guide us, our God with us join-ing, Or-
3. (ff) We all do ex-tol Thee, Thou lead-er in bat-tle, And

chas-tens and has-tens His will to make known; The wick-ed op-
dain-ing, main-tain-ing His king-dom di-vine; So from the be-
pray that Thou still our De-fend-er wilt be. Let Thy con-gre-

press-ing cease them from dis-tress-ing, Sing prais-es to His
gin-ning the fight we were win-ning, Thou, Lord, wast at our
ga-tion es-cape trib-u-la-tion; Thy name be ev-er

1, 2, 3. AFTER LAST VERSE

name, He for-gets not His own.
side, Let the glo-ry be Thine!
praised! And Thy peo-ple be free. Ev-er be free!

The Aviator

Study Song - School Choir

M. JOSEPHINE MORONEY

ELMER S. HOSMER

Con moto

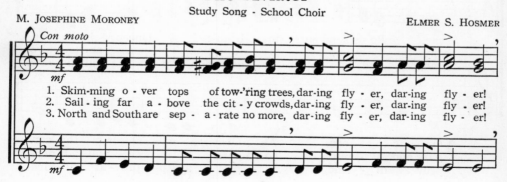

mf

1. Skim-ming o-ver tops of tow-'ring trees, dar-ing fly-er, dar-ing fly-er!
2. Sail-ing far a-bove the cit-y crowds, dar-ing fly-er, dar-ing fly-er!
3. North and South are sep-a-rate no more, dar-ing fly-er, dar-ing fly-er!

mf

Soar-ing high a - bove the crest-ed seas, dar-ing fly - er, dar-ing fly - er!
On - ward far - ing through the dark'ning clouds, dar-ing fly - er, dar-ing fly - er!
East and West now call from shore to shore, dar-ing fly - er, dar-ing fly - er!

Dis - tance now is con-quered, lev-eled Time and Space, Youth de - fies all dan - ger,
Sweep-ing past the ice - bergs, cir-cling o'er the Pole, Seek-ing new ad - ven-tures,
Rid - ing on the storm-winds, buf-fet-ing the gales, Sight-ing lands un - chart-ed,

meets it face to face. Daunt-less a - vi - a - tor, Knights of old sa - lute thee,
know-ledge still thy goal. Daunt-less a - vi - a - tor, Lo, To - day sa - lutes thee,
blaz - ing out new trails. Daunt-less a - vi - a - tor, Fu - ture years sa - lute thee,

Verses
1 and 3 Claim thee as their own and bid thee hail, All hail!
2 Claims thee as its own and bids thee hail,

bid thee hail,
bids thee hail,

Kubey-Rembrandt Studios, Phila.

J. WALTER GUETTER PLAYING THE BASSOON

Theme
Entrance of the Tradesmen, from "Midsummer Night's Dream"

BASSOONS

FELIX MENDELSSOHN-BARTHOLDY

Allegro molto

Where God Hath Walked

Eda Lou Walton

Reading Song

Étienne Henri Méhul
From the Opera, "Joseph"

Where God hath walked Val - leys shall be ex - alt - ed,
Where God shall speak Cit - ies rise in their splen - dor,

Where God hath walked Hills bow low. Where God hath trod
Where God shall speak Tow - ers blaze. Where God hath trod

Moun - tains tow - er, Ra - diant the heav'ns, Bright the ground.
Streets un - end - ing Run their long way Toward the sun.

Two by Two
Study Song

Wilbur Weeks

Johann Strauss

Tempo di mazurka

When comes the sum-mer weath-er, Pur-ple and soft the heath-er,

Out in the mead-ow gay Let us all dance a-way;

There while the breeze is play-ing, O-ver the grass-es sway-ing;

Two by two, fast then slow, round we will go.

The Old Oaken Bucket
Reading Song

Samuel Woodworth

How dear to this heart are the scenes of my child-hood, When fond rec-ol-
The or-chard, the mead-ow, the deep tan-gled wild-wood, And ev-'ry loved

D. S. The old oak-en buck-et, the i-ron-bound buck-et, The moss-cov-ered

From a crayon drawing by Henry Turner Bailey

THE OLD OAKEN BUCKET PLACE, AT GREENBUSH, MASSACHUSETTS

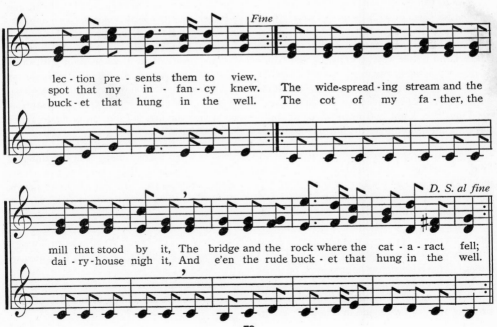

Why We Study Music

Did you ever ask yourself why we study music in school, when we might be spending the time on geography, arithmetic, or history?

There are three main reasons for studying music, and many others of less importance. One reason is that in this way we add to our enjoyment of school life. The music period brings a pleasant change from our other work. We like to sing together.

A second reason for studying music is that if we learn to know some of the most beautiful songs, we are going to find greater joy in singing and in hearing fine music after we leave school. We also want to know why some songs are more beautiful than others. As we join in singing the better songs we grow to appreciate them and to love them.

In this way we learn what excellent music is. We cultivate our taste for the best. We get some standards of comparison, so that when we hear all kinds of music, vocal and instrumental, at home, in church, at concerts, or anywhere else, we can more easily tell whether we are listening to something very choice, or to poor, trivial music which lacks real beauty and lasting charm.

Only a few of us will ever earn our living as professional musicians or music teachers; but all through life we shall be hearing music. We study music, then, both for the pleasure it gives us now, and also for the increased happiness we shall have in later years through the steady growth of our taste for the best.

A third reason why we study music is that we may add to the pleasure of others, by singing and playing for them or with them. We have to live and work together in this world, so we ought to learn how to live and work together happily and effectively. Each of us expects to do his level best, and at the same time be willing to coöperate for the general good. This is real teamwork. There is no better way of applying the true spirit of teamwork than in association with other people in playing or singing beautiful music. The better we can do our own part, the more we can give to the performance. So we study to improve our voices, learning how to produce tones that are rich, flexible, and pleasing instead of hard and strident. We also try to add to the store of good music we know and to increase our skill in singing and playing, not only in order to enrich our own musical enjoyment, but also to increase the pleasure we can give.

We cannot expect to enjoy music to the full, unless we learn a great many songs of different kinds: — patriotic songs, marching songs, folk songs, compositions both classical and modern, choice melodies and harmonies that have given deep pleasure to many people. We need to know how to think musical ideas, and how to write and read these musical thoughts. So we practice reading music from the printed page. The more easily we can read music, the wider is our command of the rich resources of musical literature. Playing an instrument is another way of enjoying music. Our satisfaction is further increased if we can compose music of our own. We also learn interesting facts about the musicians who composed the songs we sing, and the selections to which we listen. This adds to our appreciation of the music itself.

In these ways we are building up a store of enjoyment for the present, and for many years to come, for both ourselves and our friends; and at the same time we are adding to the pleasure and profit of the days we spend in school.

Questions for Thought and Discussion

1. For several years you have been studying music. Have you ever tried to think what this has meant to you?

2. What songs did you like best two or three years ago?

3. What songs do you like best now?

4. Why do you like these songs better than those of the lower grades?

5. What do you hear in music now that you could not hear before?

6. What can you do now that you could not do then?

7. In what ways do you sing better than you did when you were in the fourth or fifth grades?

8. Are some of the songs in this book better than some you have heard outside of school? Of all the songs learned in and out of school, which ones do you like best? Why?

9. Are there any of the following songs you do not know: America, Silent Night, Holy Night, Brahms' Lullaby, The Harp That Once through Tara's Halls, Juanita, Abide with Me, Yankee Doodle, Dixie, My Old Kentucky Home, Columbia, the Gem of the Ocean, All through the Night, Auld Lang Syne, Santa Lucia, Now the Day Is Over, Come Thou Almighty King, Old Black Joe, Annie Laurie, Battle Hymn of the Republic, America, the Beautiful?

Each of these songs is widely known and loved. What are the qualities which have brought this about? Is the song distinguished by beautiful melody? Rich harmony? Rhythmic appeal? Patriotic, religious, or sentimental appeal? Association with home experiences? Does it tell a story? You will find in some songs a combination of these qualities. Can you suggest other possible appeals?

10. Can you find another song in the book which matches the particular appeal of each of the above songs?

11. Choose three words to describe each of these pieces of music: Waltz in A-flat, p. 59; Largo, "New World" Symphony, 38; Dance of the Happy Spirits, 10; Andante Cantabile from the String Quartet, 53; Kelvin Grove, 15; How to Tell Wild Animals, 24; Twilight Song, 30; The Last Rose of Summer, 36; Santa Lucia, 44; The Rose-Tree, 45; Christmas Carol, 47; Now the Day Is Over, 49; The King of China's Daughter, 50; The Plaint of the Camel, 54; Where God Hath Walked, 71; Traümerei, Schumann; The Beautiful Blue Danube, Strauss; Marche Militaire, Schubert; Minuet, "Don Juan," Mozart.

Some of the following words may apply, but you may find still better ones: sad, gay, quiet, boisterous, thoughtful, peaceful, weird, sweet, plaintive, solemn, dainty, martial, heroic, majestic, lively, vigorous, sentimental, happy, mournful, angry, mysterious, pastoral, calm, fanciful, sublime, fantastic, restful, devotional, brilliant, humorous, wistful.

12. Can you name any values, in addition to the following, which you or your classmates are obtaining from your music study? *a.* Pleasure in singing. *b.* Relaxation from other school work. *c.* Development of appreciation for the best music. *d.* Learning how to read music easily. *e.* Learning how to play an instrument. *f.* Learning what teamwork means, by singing or playing together. *g.* Increasing the range of acquaintance with fine musical selections. *h.* Learning to compose music. *i.* Learning to compare musical selections and to point out their differences. *j.* Learning to find pleasure in music that other people consider superior. *k.* Improving the quality of voice and of diction.

The Fairy Ring

Study Song

From Supplementary Song Series, No. 3

AMBROISE THOMAS, from "MIGNON"

1. Let us laugh and let us sing, Dancing in a merry
2. Like the sea-sons of the year, Round we cir-cle glad-ly
3. Spring and Sum-mer glide a-way, Au-tumn comes with tress-es
4. Fast-er! fast-er! round we go, While our cheeks like ros-es

ring; We'll be fair-ies on the green, Sport-ing round the fair-y queen.
here; I'll be Sum-mer, you'll be Spring, Danc-ing in a fair-y ring.
gay; Win-ter, hand in hand with Spring, Danc-ing in a fair-y ring.
glow; Free as birds up-on the wing, Danc-ing in a fair-y ring.

John Highlandman

Reading Song

ROBERT BURNS

SCOTCH FOLK SONG

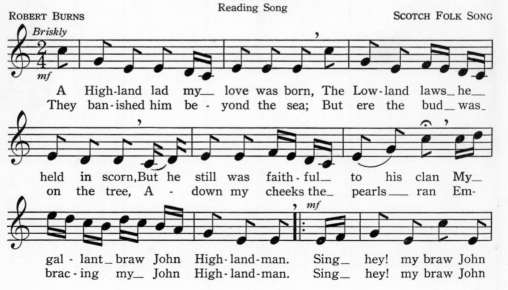

A High-land lad my love was born, The Low-land laws he
They ban-ished him be-yond the sea; But ere the bud was

held in scorn, But he still was faith-ful to his clan My
on the tree, A-down my cheeks the pearls ran Em-

gal-lant braw John High-land-man. Sing hey! my braw John
brac-ing my John High-land-man. Sing hey! my braw John

High-land-man, Sing ho! my braw John— High-land-man, There's

no' a lad—in— a' the land Was match wi'— my— John High-land-man.

Fairy Bells
Reading Song

ANN UNDERHILL

E. G. GEIJER

Hark the bell, Fair-y bell, Faint-ly sound-ing— Down the —dell.

Hark the bell, Fair-y bell,

Ring-ing clear, Chim-ing near, Weav-ing soft its— sweet mag-ic spell.

Ring-ing clear, Chim-ing near, sweet spell.

Tone Blending

TARANTELLA, BY SINDING

Tarantella

Study Song 220

ETHEL C. BROWN

Allegretto

ITALIAN FOLK SONG

Whirling and twirling and singing and laughing, Stamping, tramping and chattering,
Dance a-gain, prance a-gain, tambourine sing-ing, Flick-ing, click-ing the cas-ta-nets

chaff-ing; Whirl - ing and twirl - ing and sing - ing and laugh - ing, Stamp - ing,
ring - ing; Dance a - gain, prance a - gain, tam - bou - rine sing - ing, Flick - ing,

tramp-ing and chat-ter-ing, chaff - ing; Where are there men who are strong-er and
click-ing the cas - ta - nets ring - ing; Loom-ing and gloom-ing the moun-tain a-

78

fleet - er, Where are there maids who are fair - er and sweet-er? Where are there
bove us, Here to you, cheer to you, maid-ens who love us; Loom-ing and

men who are strong-er and fleet - er, Where are there maids who are fair - er and
gloom-ing the moun-tain a - bove us, Here to you, cheer to you, maid-ens who

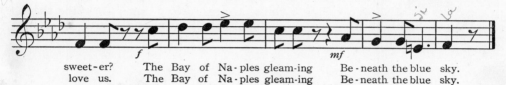

sweet-er? The Bay of Na - ples gleam-ing Be - neath the blue sky.
love us. The Bay of Na - ples gleam-ing Be - neath the blue sky.

The Night Will Never Stay

Reading Song

ELEANOR FARJEON   HOWARD HANSON

The night will nev-er stay, The night will still go by, Though with a mil-lion stars

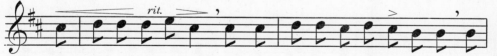

You pin it to the sky, Though you bind it with a blow-ing wind And

buck-le it with the moon, The night will slip a - way Like sor-row or a tune.

Twilight
Reading Song

EDA LOU WALTON

A. DANHAUSER

Twi - light fall - ing, birds_ are_ nest - ing, breez - es rest - ing,
Shad - ows lift - ing, sil - v'ring hills now, sil - v'ring rills now,

Stars are peep - ing, hills__ are sleep - ing in the shade.
Moon - light drift - ing lights_ the heav'ns and earth be - low.

O Country Great and Glorious
Reading Song

The Modern Music Series

ROBERT SCHUMANN

O coun - try great and glo - rious, O dear and hap - py land, Thy faith - ful chil - dren
Be right - eous - ness thy hel - met, Be mer - cy thy good shield, Be jus - tice keen the_

serve thee With_heart and voice_ and hand. Thy sons they stand a - bout thee, Strong
weap - on, Thy_ no - ble arm_doth wield. Be truth thy shin - ing ar - mor, O

bul-warks of the state; They guard thy tow'rs vic-to-rious, Thy walls in - vi - o - late.
coun-try, glorious, great, And count-less gen -e - ra - tions Thy fame shall cel-e-brate.

O coun-try great and glo-rious, O dear and hap-py land, Thy faith - ful chil-dren__

serve thee With heart   and voice__and hand, With heart, with heart and voice and hand.

The Vagabond's Life

Reading Song

NANCY BYRD TURNER

POLISH FOLK DANCE

Lively

Come, now, fol-low as I   lead the way, All roads beck-on when the heart is gay!
Sun-light spar-kles and the wind is high, Good folks greet us as we   wan-der by!

Tell your for-tune? if you have a rid - dle Bring it quick to the gyp - sy gay;
Tam-bou-rine and cas-ta-net and fid - dle, Sing and dance all the bright, glad day!

Evening Prayer

Study Song - School Choir

FREDERICK H. MARTENS

ENGELBERT HUMPERDINCK
from "Hansel and Gretel"

ENGELBERT HUMPERDINCK

When a-way to bed I creep, Four-teen an-gels watch my__ sleep; Two my head pro-tect-ing, Two my feet di-rect-ing, Two up-on my right hand, Two up-on my left hand, Two me warm-ly cov-er, Two a-bove me hov-er,

Two up-on my right hand, Two up-on my__ left hand, Two me warm-ly cov-er Two a-bove me

D *cresc.*   *poco rit.*

Two are ev - er bid - ing, My way to heav - en guid - - ing.

hov - er, Two my way to heav - en guid - - ing.

God Be Our Guide

Reading Song

From the German   Franz Abt

Moderato

1. God be our guide, His help is sure; In Him our hope shall
2. Work that we pur - pose ev - 'ry hour Can pros - per on - ly
3. Might-y - to bless from day to day, Till life's brief light shall

rest___ se - cure; His strength a-lone suc - cess can bring; This
through___ His power; Our souls His gra - cious pres - ence seek; With
pass___ a - way, He gives and takes, and works His will; We

prayer from ev - 'ry heart shall spring, God be our guide, God be our guide.
joy - ful lips this prayer we speak, God be our guide, God be our guide.
pray, and bid our hearts be still. God be our guide, God be our guide.

Hungarian Dancing Song
Rote Song

The Modern Music Series

HUNGARIAN FOLK SONG

Rather slowly, increasing in speed

Two_____ and two, the danc-ers spright-ly, Turn_____ and poise and whirl so
Life_____ is full of hope and pleas-ure; While_____ we tread this joc-und

light-ly, Hair_____ and rib-bons gai-ly fly-ing, Feet with swal-lows'
meas-ure, Hap - py girl and jo-vial boy,_____ Let us all our

wings_____ are vy-ing; Danc-ing, danc-ing, Gay, ah!_____ so gay_ are_we.
youth_____ en - joy._____ Danc-ing, danc-ing, Gay, ah!_____ so gay_ are_we.

Planting Poppies
Reading Song

From the Russian,
by NATHAN HASKELL DOLE

RUSSIAN FOLK SONG,
arranged by A. GRETCHANINOFF

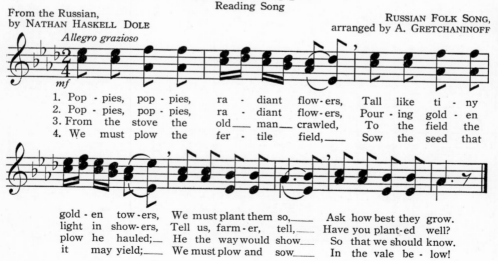

Allegro grazioso

1. Pop - pies, pop - pies, ra - diant flow-ers, Tall like ti - ny
2. Pop - pies, pop - pies, ra - diant flow-ers, Pour - ing gold - en
3. From the stove the old_ man_ crawled, To the field the
4. We must plow the fer - tile field, Sow the seed that

gold - en tow-ers, We must plant them so,_____ Ask how best they grow.
light in show-ers, Tell us, farm - er, tell,_____ Have you plant-ed well?
plow he hauled;_____ He the way would show_____ So that we should know.
it may yield;_____ We must plow and sow_____ In the vale be - low!

The House in the Wood

Reading Song

MAX HINÜBER

E. HERMES

Moderato

1. Tread soft-ly, light-ly here, Birds build their nests a - near;
2. Winds mur-mur lull - a - bies, Boughs, rock-ing, fall and rise;
3. Here first will nest - lings fly While yet the nest is nigh;

Where boughs of oak and beech Wave high__ and out of reach, Where
Leaves, rust - ling, whis-per low What on - ly birds may know; All
Here first__ will learn to trill Such songs__ as love doth thrill; Till

cresc. *dim.*

leaves pro-tect, pro-tect from rain, From sun and__rain, From sun and__rain.
here__ is safe, is safe, se-cure From hawk and__lure, From hawk and__lure.
from their for - est, for - est home, They long to__roam, They long__to__roam.

cresc. *dim.*

pro - tect_____ from rain,
is safe,_____ se -cure
their for - est home,

Who Has Seen the Wind?

Study Song - School Choir

CHRISTINA ROSSETTI

MRS. H. H. A. BEACH

MRS. H. H. A. BEACH

Who has seen the wind?

Neith - er I nor you;

But when the leaves hang

trem - bling, The wind is pass - ing through.

Who has seen the wind? Neith-er you nor I; But when the leaves bow

down their heads, The wind is pass - ing by.

Old Black Joe

Reading Song

STEPHEN COLLINS FOSTER   STEPHEN COLLINS FOSTER

Moderato
ALTOS

1. Gone are the days when my heart was young and gay Gone are my
2. Why do I weep when my heart should feel no pain? Why do I
3. Where are the hearts once so hap - py and so free? The chil - dren so

friends from the cot - ton fields a - way; Gone from the earth to a
sigh that my friends come not a - gain? Griev - ing for forms now de-
dear that I held up - on my knee? Gone to the shore where my

bet - ter land I know, I hear their gen - tle voic - es call - ing,
part - ed long a - go, I hear their gen - tle voic - es call - ing,
soul has longed to go, I hear their gen - tle voic - es call - ing,

"Old Black Joe". I'm com-ing, I'm com-ing, For my head is bend-ing low; I

hear their gen - tle voic - es call - ing, "Old Black Joe."

The American Hymn

Reading Song

MATTHIAS KELLER · MATTHIAS KELLER

1. Speed our Re - pub - lic, O Fa - ther on high, Lead us in
2. Fore - most in bat - tle, for Free - dom to stand, We rush to
3. Rise up, proud ea - gle, rise up to the clouds! Spread thy broad

path - ways of jus - tice and right! Rul - ers as well as the
arms when a - roused by its call; Still, as of yore when George
wings o'er this fair west - ern world! Fling from thy beak our dear

ruled, one and all, Gir - dle with vir - tue, the ar - mor of might!
Wash - ing - ton led, Thun - ders our war cry, "We con - quer or fall!"
ban - ner of old! Show that it still is for free - dom un - furled!

Hail! three times hail__ to our coun-try and flag! Rul-ers as
Hail! three times hail__ to our coun-try and flag! Still, as of
Hail! three times hail__ to our coun-try and flag! Fling from thy

well as the ruled, one and all, Gir-dle with vir-tue, the
yore when George Wash-ing-ton led, Thun-ders our war__cry, "We
beak our dear ban-ner of old! Show that it still__ is for

ar-mor of might! Hail! three times hail__to our coun-try and flag!
con-quer or fall!" Hail! three times hail__to our coun-try and flag!
free-dom un-furled! Hail! three times hail__to our coun-try and flag!

Tone Blending

The Brooklet

Study Song

WILHELM MÜLLER

FRANZ SCHUBERT

I____ heard a brook-let mur-mur A - down its rock-y____ height, In -
I____ fol - low ev - er on - ward While still the brook-let___ near, And___

to the val-ley flow - ing, So___ won-drous fresh and bright. I know not how it
bright-er gleam its wa - ters, More bright and yet___ more clear. Oh, tell me, brook-let

hap - pened, Or____ who the im - pulse gave, But I must fol - low____
whith - er Thou___ lur - est me to - day? Thou hast with thy___ sweet___

down - ward, Must take my walk - ing___ stave,___ But I must fol - low____
sing - ing En - ticed my soul a - way,___ Thou hast with thy___ sweet

down - ward, Must take my walk - ing___ stave, But___ I must fol - low
sing - ing En - ticed my soul a - way, Thou hast with thy sweet

down-ward, Must take my walk - ing___ stave, Take___ my___ stave, Take my stave.___
sing - ing En - ticed my soul_ a - way, Far_ a - way, Far a - way.____

Courtesy of Rudolf Lesch, New York

THE OLD WATERMILL, BY HOBBEMA

Wandering

Reading Song

TRADITIONAL

FRANZ SCHUBERT

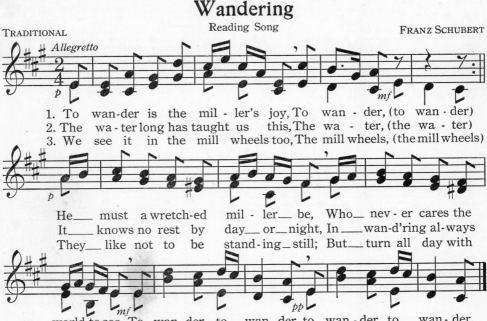

1. To wan-der is the mil-ler's joy, To wan-der, (to wan-der)
2. The wa-ter long has taught us this, The wa-ter, (the wa-ter)
3. We see it in the mill wheels too, The mill wheels, (the mill wheels)

He___ must a wretch-ed mil-ler___ be, Who___ nev-er cares the
It___ knows no rest by day___ or___ night, In ___ wan-d'ring al-ways
They___ like not to be stand-ing___ still; But___ turn all day with

world to see, To wan-der, to ___ wan-der, to wan-der, to ___ wan-der.
takes de-light, The wa-ter, the___ wa-ter, the wa-ter, the___ wa-ter.
right good will, The mill wheels, the mill wheels, the mill wheels, the mill wheels.

91

The Fishermen

Study Song

Ann Underhill

Jean Baptiste Wekerlin

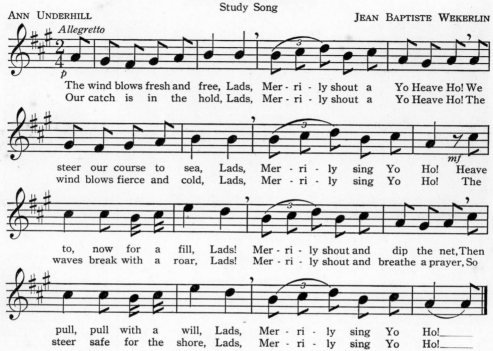

Allegretto

The wind blows fresh and free, Lads, Mer-ri-ly shout a Yo Heave Ho! We
Our catch is in the hold, Lads, Mer-ri-ly shout a Yo Heave Ho! The

steer our course to sea, Lads, Mer-ri-ly sing Yo Ho! Heave
wind blows fierce and cold, Lads, Mer-ri-ly sing Yo Ho! The

to, now for a fill, Lads! Mer-ri-ly shout and dip the net, Then
waves break with a roar, Lads! Mer-ri-ly shout and breathe a prayer, So

pull, pull with a will, Lads, Mer-ri-ly sing Yo Ho!____
steer safe for the shore, Lads, Mer-ri-ly sing Yo Ho!____

Green Holiday

Reading Song

Aldis Dunbar

Polish Folk Song

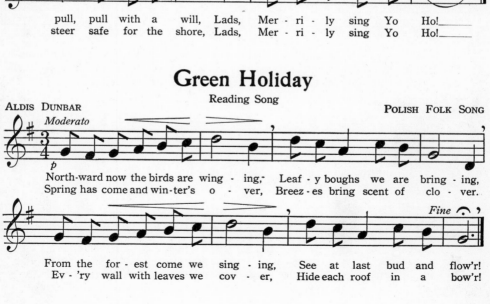

Moderato

North-ward now the birds are wing-ing,- Leaf-y boughs we are bring-ing,
Spring has come and win-ter's o-ver, Breez-es bring scent of clo-ver.

Fine

From the for-est come we sing-ing, See at last bud and flow'r!
Ev-'ry wall with leaves we cov-er, Hide each roof in a bow'r!

Now no more the i-cy breez-es from the North-land blow,

Now no more we need to has-ten through the snow. For

D.C. al 🔂

Farandole
Reading Song

ALDIS DUNBAR OLD FRENCH MELODY

Gaily

Swing high, gay wo-ven gar-land; Swing low, flow'rs as we pass.
Light feet, fol-low our danc-ing; June comes, o-ver the grass.

O-pen your door and come out to-day, Join in our
Cir-cle and curve on the King's High-way, Wind through the

far-an-dole sum-mer is glow-ing; Sing in the sun-shine, all who
lanes with a car-ol-ling clear. Down in the gar-den bright with

fol-low, This is our hour for laugh-ter and glee; Blithe-heart and
ros-es, Ech-o our song by trel-lis and tree. Wel-come the

mer-ry-heart, come a-way, Join in our far-an-dole, blos-soms are blow-ing;
sum-mer with meas-ures gay; This is our hap-pi-est time of the year.

The Bolero

Reading Song

FLEUR CONKLING

SPANISH MELODY

Tempo di Bolero

Ring - ing tam - bou - rines, Click - ing cas - ta - nets
Scar - let ros - es___ fling, Gay - est songs we___ sing,

Rhyth - mic sways our___ dance, Whirl - ing steps en - trance!
Twirl - ing fast the___ tune, End - ed all too___ soon!

My Pocket

Reading Song

From the original Hungarian
by GRACE L. WALKER

ANNA VON WOHLFARTH-GRILLE

Quickly (Rustico)

Ti - ny pock - et, so small, Far too small for this roll; If I nib - ble
Cross is Bob - by with me, Will no long - er tease me. Gra-cious, I am

one bite It will still be too tight; Why not swal-low it whole?
so sad, Bob - by, do not stay mad! Come now, Bob - by, tease me!

Tone Blending

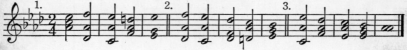

Caraway and Cheese

From the original Hungarian
by GRACE L. WALKER

Study Song

ANNA VON WOHLFARTH-GRILLE

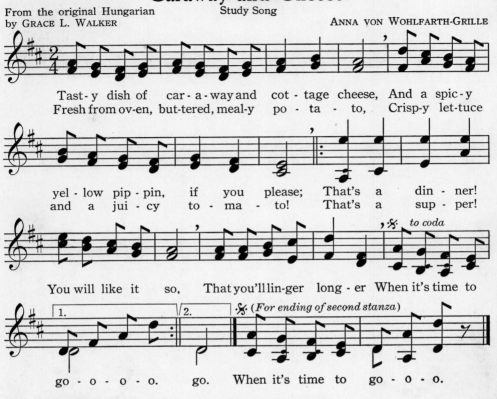

Tast-y dish of car-a-way and cot-tage cheese, And a spic-y
Fresh from ov-en, but-tered, meal-y po-ta-to, Crisp-y let-tuce

yel-low pip-pin, if you please; That's a din-ner!
and a jui-cy to-ma-to! That's a sup-per!

You will like it so, That you'll lin-ger long-er When it's time to

to coda

1.
2.
(For ending of second stanza)

go-o-o-o. go. When it's time to go-o-o.

The Bell Doth Toll

Three-Part Round

TRADITIONAL

OLD ROUND

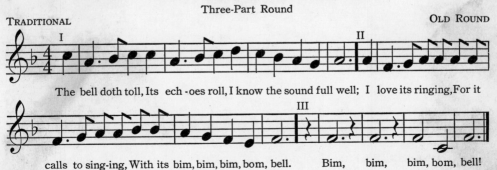

The bell doth toll, Its ech-oes roll, I know the sound full well; I love its ringing, For it

calls to sing-ing, With its bim, bim, bim, bom, bell. Bim, bim, bim, bom, bell!

March
Reading Song

WILLIAM CULLEN BRYANT   HOWARD HANSON

The storm-y March is come at last With wind, and cloud, and chang-ing skies; I

hear the rush-ing of the blast That through the snow-y val-ley flies. Ah,

pass-ing few are those who speak, Wild, storm-y month, in praise of thee, Yet,

though thy winds are loud and bleak, Thou art a wel-come month to me. For

thou to north-ern lands a-gain The glad and glo-rious sun dost bring, And

thou hast joined the gen-tle rain And wear'st the gen-tle name of spring.

WENDELL HOSS PLAYING THE FRENCH HORN

Theme
Nocturne from "Midsummer Night's Dream"

FRENCH HORN   FELIX MENDELSSOHN-BARTHOLDY

By the Waves

Reading Song

MARGARET E. SANGSTER

WILHELM PETERSON-BERGER

1. Crisp and curl - ing, Soft__ un - furl - ing, Caps of sil - ver__ foam,_____ Haste the break - ers, Frol - ic - mak - ers, Chas-ing play - mates home._____
2. Wave - lets cream - ing, Sun - shine gleam - ing, In the shin - ing__ sands;_____ Gay and mer - ry, Bold and cheer - y Delve the sun - burn'd hands._____
3. Drift - ing, lift - ing, Rift - ing, sift - ing, 'Neath the smil - ing__ sky;_____ On the shin - gle* Pleas-ures min - gle, And the day__ goes__ by._____

* coarse gravel at the seashore

Annie Laurie

Reading Song

DOUGLAS OF FINGLAND

LADY JOHN SCOTT

1. Max - wel-ton's braes are bon-nie, Where___ ear-ly fa's the___
2. Her___ brow is like the snow-drift, Her___ throat is like the___
3. Like___ dew on th' gow-an ly - ing Is th' fa' o' her fair - y___

dew, And 'twas there that An-nie Lau-rie Gave me her prom-ise true;
swan; Her___ face it is the fair-est That e'er the sun shone on,
feet, And like winds in sum-mer sigh-ing, Her voice is low and sweet,

Gave me her prom - ise true, Which ne'er for-got will be,
That e'er the sun shone on, And___ dark blue is her e'e,
Her voice is low and sweet, And she's a' the world to me,

And for bon - nie An - nie Lau - rie I'd___ lay___ me doon___ and dee.

Forth to the Meadows

From the German

Reading Song

FRANZ SCHUBERT
from "ROSAMUNDE"

FRANZ SCHUBERT

Allegretto

Forth to the mead - ows, ye
Ech - oes are ring - ing from

fair mer - ry maid - ens,
green loft - y moun - tains,

Haste to the mead-ows to dance and to play; Yield to the witch - ing de-
Pleas-ure and glad-ness now have no al - loy; Forth then ye maid - ens, to

lights of — the spring - time,   Glad - ness and pleas - ure a - wait us to - day.
flow'r sprin-kled mead - ows   Join in our pleas - ures with love and with joy.

My Golden Fish

From the Russian, by
NATHAN HASKELL DOLE

Reading Song

RUSSIAN FOLK SONG, arranged by
A. GRETCHANINOFF

Allegro non troppo

1. Here's a   fish I've — caught, Here's a —   gold - en — fish I've caught! Here's a
2. I   will   bear my — fish,   I will —   bear my — gold - en   fish, I will
3. To   a   maid - en — fair,   To a —   maid - en — fair I'll go,   To a

gold - en fish I've caught in my   net,   I will bear my gold - en   fish   on my   back!
bear my gold-en fish   on my   back, To a maid-en fair I'll   go with my   fish.
maid-en fair I'll   go with my   fish, May-be then she'll be my   wife,   be my   wife!

Tone Blending

A Wind Awoke

Study Song - School Choir

Colin Sterne

H. Ernest Nichol

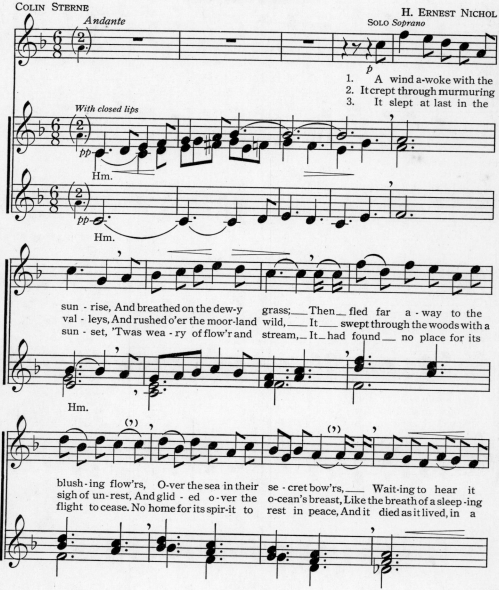

1. A wind a-woke with the sun-rise, And breathed on the dew-y grass;— Then fled far a-way to the blush-ing flow'rs, O-ver the sea in their se-cret bow'rs,— Wait-ing to hear it

2. It crept through murmuring val-leys, And rushed o'er the moor-land wild,— It swept through the woods with a sigh of un-rest, And glid-ed o-ver the o-cean's breast, Like the breath of a sleep-ing

3. It slept at last in the sun-set, 'Twas wea-ry of flow'r and stream,— It had found no place for its flight to cease. No home for its spir-it to rest in peace, And it died as it lived, in a

With closed lips

Hm.

pass,_____ Wait-ing to hear__ it pass,___ To hear it pass.
child,_____ The breath of a sleep-ing child,__ A sleep-ing child.
dream,_____ It died as it lived, in a dream,_ A dream, a dream.

The Snake Charmer
Reading Song

MARY J. M. LARKIN   TYPICAL AIR OF HINDUSTAN

Down the street comes the jug-gler man, Charm-er of snakes in Hin-du-stan,
See that big co - bra raise its head, Spec-ta-cled hoods now be - gin to spread,

Tur - ban, dhu - ti, rust - y hue, Weird, sweet mu - sic, pi - ping too;
Four and twen - ty dance I am sure, Danc - ing to the mag - ic lure;

Lift the lids of your bas - kets, do, Fa - mous mag - i - cal Hin - du;
Bead - y eyes on the charm - er fix As__ he pipes on his pun - ji,

Show the tricks your nag-as do, Show us what they can do, Hin - du.____
Fee him well for now he's through; Hap-py the Nat__ sa - laams to_____ you.__

dhuti = trousers; nagas = snakes; punji = gourd flute; Nat = snake charmer; salaams = bows.

Were I the Sun

Reading Song

A. R. WELLS

MARGARET RUTHVEN LANG

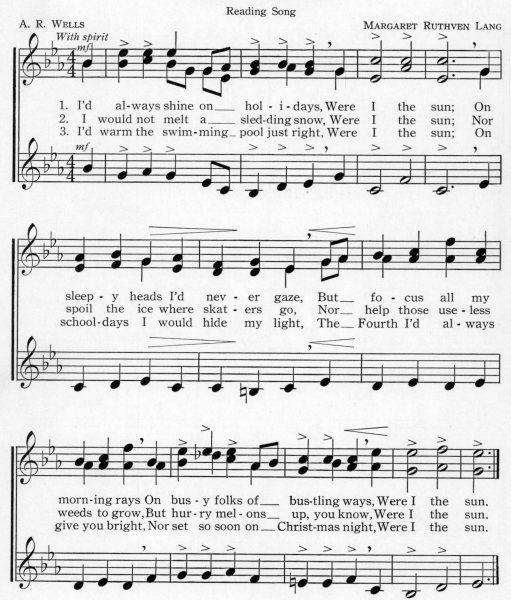

1. I'd al-ways shine on___ hol - i - days, Were I the sun; On
2. I would not melt a___ sled-ding snow, Were I the sun; Nor
3. I'd warm the swim-ming_ pool just right, Were I the sun; On

sleep - y heads I'd nev - er gaze, But__ fo - cus all my
spoil the ice where skat - ers go, Nor__ help those use - less
school-days I would hide my light, The__ Fourth I'd al - ways

morn-ing rays On bus - y folks of___ bus-tling ways, Were I the sun.
weeds to grow, But hur - ry mel - ons__ up, you know, Were I the sun.
give you bright, Nor set so soon on__ Christ-mas night, Were I the sun.

Largo

Study Song - School Choir

From the opera, *Xerxes,* by
GEORGE FREDERICK HANDEL

THOMAS WILLIAMS

Fa - ther in heav'n, Thy chil - dren hear,

As they a - dor - ing bow, O Thou Al - might - y One, Our weak-ness

heed; Strength - en our faith; With hope in - spire our hearts, Flam-ing our

souls with love Like un - to Thine. Then shall Thy works a-bound, Men

shall pro - claim that God our Lord is God a-lone, And

ho - ly, ho - ly is His name, And ho - ly is His name;

God our Lord is God a-lone, And ho - ly, ho - ly is His name.

Words by permission of C. C. Birchard and Company

Star of Peace

Traditional

Reading Song

J. E. Gould

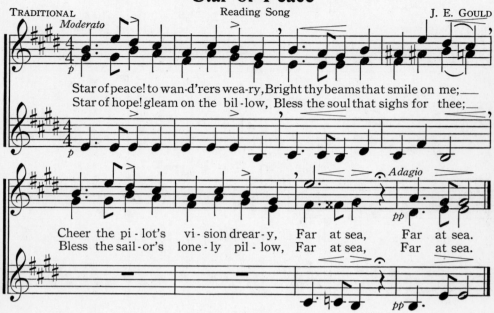

Star of peace! to wan-d'rers wea-ry, Bright thy beams that smile on me;___
Star of hope! gleam on the bil-low, Bless the soul that sighs for thee;___

Cheer the pi-lot's vi-sion drear-y, Far at sea, Far at sea.
Bless the sail-or's lone-ly pil-low, Far at sea, Far at sea.

April! April!

Study Song

DORA READ GOODALE

WILLIAM G. HAMMOND

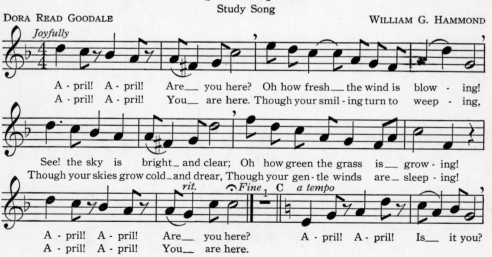

A-pril! A-pril! Are___ you here? Oh how fresh___ the wind is blow-ing!
A-pril! A-pril! You___ are here. Though your smil-ing turn to weep-ing,

See! the sky is bright___ and clear; Oh how green the grass is___ grow-ing!
Though your skies grow cold___ and drear, Though your gen-tle winds are___ sleep-ing!

A-pril! A-pril! Are___ you here? A-pril! A-pril! Is___ it you?
A-pril! A-pril! You___ are here.

See how fair the flow'rs are___ spring - ing! Sun is warm and brooks are___clear;

Oh how glad the birds are___ sing - ing! A - pril! A - pril! Is it___you?

What Do We Plant?

Reading Song

HENRY ABBEY   JOHANN FRIEDRICH REICHARDT

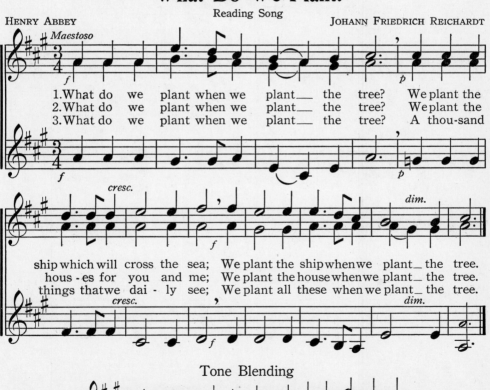

1. What do we plant when we plant___ the tree? We plant the
2. What do we plant when we plant___ the tree? We plant the
3. What do we plant when we plant___ the tree? A thou-sand

ship which will cross the sea; We plant the ship when we plant___ the tree.
hous - es for you and me; We plant the house when we plant___ the tree.
things that we dai - ly see; We plant all these when we plant___ the tree.

Tone Blending

Friendship
Reading Song

Translated from the German

WOLFGANG AMADEUS MOZART

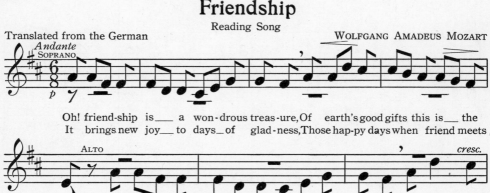

Oh! friend-ship is ___ a won-drous treas-ure, Of earth's good gifts this is ___ the
It brings new joy ___ to days ___ of glad-ness, Those hap-py days when friend meets

best, It sweet-ens life, ___ and none can meas-ure How those pos-
friend; In days ___ of grief ___ it tem-pers sad-ness And brings de-

ses-sing it ___ are blest. In joy, in sor-row, Friendship cheers, And chang-es
lights that nev-er end. It mat-ters not how dark the day, If Friend-ship

not with chang-ing years, And chang-es ___ not with chang-ing ___ years.
cheers us on ___ our way, If Friend-ship ___ cheers us ___ on our ___ way.

Shall I Sing?
Reading Song

KATE GREENAWAY

HORATIO PARKER

"Shall I sing?" says the lark, "Shall I bloom?" says the flow'r, "Shall I

come?" says the sun, "Or shall I?" ___ says the show'r. Sing your songs,

pret - ty___ bird,___ Ros - es, bloom for___ an___ hour; ___

Shine on,___ dear-est sun, Shine on, dear-est sun, Go a - way,___ naugh-ty show'rs!

Joys of Spring
Study Song

Translated from the German

M. VOGEL

Andantino

Birds are sing-ing, flow'rs are bloom-ing, Spring's bright flags are all___ un-furled,
Joy we'll meet in ev - 'ry path-way, She doth___ sing with___ ev - 'ry bird,

Flow'rs _____ bloom, Spring's bright
Joy _____ doth sing, doth

Birds are sing-ing, flow'rs are bloom - ing, Spring's bright flags are all un-
Joy we'll meet in ev - 'ry path - way, She___ doth___ sing___ with ev - 'ry

furled. Come, oh come then, let___ us___ wan-der, Through the shad-y wood-land yon-der,
bird. Soft in flow - er - heart she's bed-ded, Hid in grass with dew be-thread-ed,

Far in___ God's wide sun-ny___ world, Far in___ God's wide sun-ny___ world.
Mur-m'ring where a___ stream-let's heard, Mur-m'ring where a stream-let's heard.

My Normandy

Reading Song

Translated from F. BÉRAT

F. BÉRAT

In spring-time when the birds are sing-ing, And hope re-turns to earth a-gain,
I've seen the moun-tain tor-rents dash-ing From snow-y peaks in Switz-er-land;

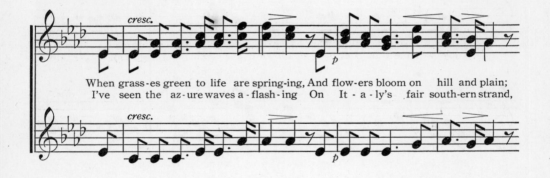

When grass-es green to life are spring-ing, And flow-ers bloom on hill and plain;
I've seen the az-ure waves a-flash-ing On It-a-ly's fair south-ern strand,

When swallows homeward bend their flight, And gone is win-ter's frost-y night, Ah!
And man-y an-oth-er ra-diant shore, That smiles in beau-ty ev-er-more. But

By Burton Holmes from Ewing Galloway, N. Y.

SPRINGTIME IN NORMANDY

then for thee my heart is yearn-ing, Dear Nor-man-dy, my own, my na-tive land.
still for thee my heart was yearn-ing, Dear Nor-man-dy, my own, my na-tive land.

Playtime in Japan

Reading Song

ALDIS DUNBAR   JAPANESE MELODY

When the snow-flakes light are fall - ing In our far Ja - pan, Then I hear my
But when blos-soms fill the gar - den, White on ev - 'ry tree, Then we hold the

play-mates call - ing, "Come, O Yu - ki San. Catch the snow and heap it high,
Feast of Ban - ners, Raise the No - bu - ri. Flags and pen - nons in the wind

Shape it like a man. Greet him as Da - ru - ma Sa - ma!" In our far Ja - pan.
Stream in bright ar - ray. See, our gold-en fish-es swimming High in air to - day.

Daruma Sama is the Japanese deity in whose image Japanese boys and girls shape their snow men.
The symbol for the "boys' festival" in Japan is a bright paper kite in the shape of a fish flown from a flagstaff.
The fish chosen is the carp, in Japanese, Noburi, because of its perseverance in swimming up stream.

Song for Arbor Day

Reading Song

From Supplementary Song Series   PETER I. TSCHAIKOWSKY

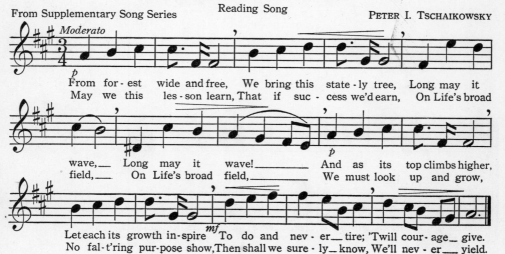

From for - est wide and free, We bring this state - ly tree, Long may it
May we this les - son learn, That if suc - cess we'd earn, On Life's broad

wave,___ Long may it wave!_____ And as its top climbs higher,
field,___ On Life's broad field,_____ We must look up and grow,

Let each its growth in - spire To do and nev - er___ tire; 'Twill cour - age_ give.
No fal - t'ring pur-pose show, Then shall we sure - ly_ know, We'll nev - er___ yield.

Gondoliera

(O SOLE MIO)

Study Song

WILBUR WEEKS　　　　　　　　　　　　　　　　　　　　　EDUARDO DI CAPUA

The sun - set　ra - diance, dream-ing wave-lets lav - ing,＿＿ The an - cient
It sings the　cit - y　'mid the wa - ters　ly - ing,＿＿ Her charm the

wa - ter - ways＿ with gold is　pav - ing,＿ From Mal - a - moc - co　ves-per bells are
cen - tu - ries＿ that pass de - fy - ing,＿ Her mar - ble　man-sions with their gar - den

ring - ing＿With sil - ver voice the song of　eve - ning　sing - ing.＿Then as the
clos - es＿That in the moon-light breathe a scent of　ros - es.＿Thus as the

twi - light＿ fades in - to　night,＿ And in the　heav - ens＿＿ the stars are
twi - light＿ fades in - to　night,＿ And in the　heav - ens＿＿ the stars are

bright,＿　The　old＿＿　ca - nals a - long, ah,＿＿ From dark gon-
bright,＿　The　old＿＿　ca - nals a - long, ah,＿＿ A　love - ly

do - las sounds a　song!＿＿
song＿＿＿＿＿＿＿＿＿＿ a　song.＿＿＿＿＿

Theme
From "Violin Sonatina"

*Reprinted by courtesy of
N. Simrock, G.m.b. H. Leipzig.*

ANTONIN DVOŘÁK
Opus 100

ANTONIN DVOŘÁK

Sweden
Reading Song

WILBUR WEEKS

SWEDISH FOLK SONG

Andante
SOLO OR SEMI-CHORUS

O North-land so old, where the high moun-tains rise, You

calm, pleas-ant coun-try, how I love you! You're fair - er than all oth - er

lands__'neath the skies, With mead-ows green and heav - en blue a-

CHORUS

bove you! With mead-ows green and heav-en blue a - bove you!

Crowning the Snow-Maiden
Reading Song

EDA LOU WALTON

FINNISH FOLK SONG

Quietly

mf

Gath - er   the   snow   blos - soms,   first   ti - ny   snow   flow'rs,
Soon   will   the   snow - maid - en   fade   in   the   sun - light,

Wreathe for   the snow maid-en's brow   love-ly gar-lands, Fash - ion   a crown, mer - ry
Soon   she will fade   in   the gleam   of the moon-light, Un - der   the snow-bank the

lads, laugh-ing las - sies;   For   win - ter now   is   done   and   spring __ will come.
mead-ows are flow - 'ring; For   win - ter now   is   done   and   spring __ will come.

Norway

Reading Song

WILBUR WEEKS

OLE BULL

Oh far to the north, in gran-deur se-rene, A moun-tain-ous coun-try is show-ing,

A moun-tain coun-try's show-ing,

The fiords dent its coast with long tongues of green, Their waves in the sun bright-ly glow-ing.

with tongues of green, Their waves in sun-light glow-ing.

Its broad sweeping slopes are white with the snow, Its streams sing their way to the o-cean

white with snow,

Tone Blending

Where, bright as the rain-bow, gla-ciers a-glow Are trem-bling in ra - diant — mo-tion.

gla-ciers glow Are trem-bling, ra - diant mo-tion.

A Child's Book

Study Song

CHARLES KEELER

RUDOLPH GANZ

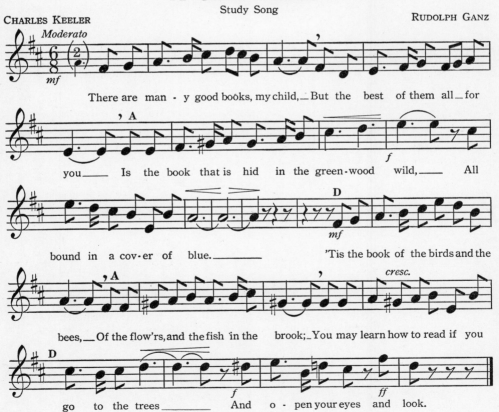

There are man - y good books, my child, — But the best of them all — for

you — Is the book that is hid in the green-wood wild, — All

bound in a cov-er of blue. ’Tis the book of the birds and the

bees, — Of the flow'rs, and the fish in the brook; — You may learn how to read if you

go to the trees And o - pen your eyes and look.

Who Hath Built Thee, Lovely Wood?

Study Song - School Choir

J. von Eichendorff

Felix Mendelssohn-Bartholdy

Allegro alla marcia

1. Who hath built thee, love - ly
2. Hushed the din the rude world
3. What the ho - ly si - lence

Felix Mendelssohn-Bartholdy

From an engraving made when he was a young man.

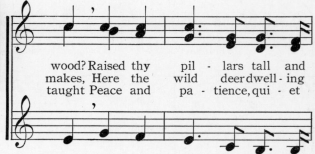

wood? Raised thy pil - lars tall and
makes, Here the wild deer dwell - ing
taught Peace and pa - tience, qui - et

slen - der? To the Mas - ter praise I'll ren - der, For His might - y work is
on - ly, And my horn in wood-ways lone - ly, Thou-sand sil - v'ry ech - oes
liv - ing, Long we'll cher - ish with thanks-giv-ing, What the bless - ed woodland

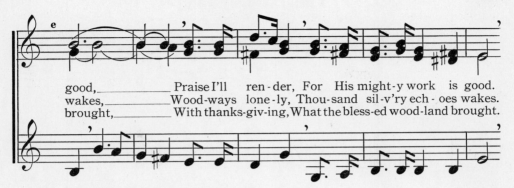

good,_____ Praise I'll ren-der, For His might-y work is good.
wakes,_____ Wood-ways lone-ly, Thou-sand sil-v'ry ech-oes wakes.
brought,_____ With thanks-giv-ing, What the bless-ed wood-land brought.

good, To the Mas-ter praise I'll ren-der,
wakes, And my horn in wood-ways lone-ly,
brought, Long we'll cher-ish with thanks-giv-ing,

Fare thee well,_____ Fare thee well,_____ Fare thee

Fare thee well,_____ Fare thee well,_____ Fare thee well,_____

Fare thee well,_____ Fare thee well,_____ Fare thee

well,_____ thou love-ly wood, Fare thee well, fare thee well, thou love-ly wood.

well,

The Nightingale

Reading Song

ALDIS DUNBAR

FRANZ LISZT

Moderato

The stars a-bove are shin-ing, While clear-ly through the vale,
From out his heart comes well-ing, Be-fore the night is gone,

In tones of thrill-ing sweet-ness I hear the night-in-gale.
A hymn of praise and glo-ry To hail the com-ing dawn.

To a Robin

Study Song - School Choir

LILLIAN MOHR

LILLIAN MOHR

Gracefully

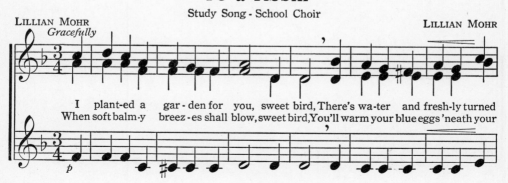

I plant-ed a gar-den for you, sweet bird, There's wa-ter and fresh-ly turned
When soft balm-y breez-es shall blow, sweet bird, You'll warm your blue eggs 'neath your

THE ANGELUS, BY MILLET

Sweet the Angelus Is Ringing

Study Song – School Choir

HENRY SMART

Sweet the An-ge-lus is ring-ing O'er the riv-er, up the dell;

Peace and rest to la-bor bring-ing, Chimes the bell, chimes the bell.

All the vine - yard bow'rs are still,___ O'er the moun - tain side,___
Si - lent sleeps the har - vest plain,___ Where the reap - ers' lay___

___ Dreams the shad - ow on the hill, Dreams up - on the tide.___
___ Rose and fell a - gain, a - gain, Through the long bright day.___

Vil - lage lights with cheer - y beam,___ Through the twi - light ___ come,___
In the cloud-land, o'er the shade,___ See the thin moon ___ lies,___

Drop - ping down the fleet - ing stream ___ Glides the fish - er home.___
Like a shin - ing sic - kle - blade ___ Rest - ing in the skies.___

Sweet the An - ge - lus is ring - ing O'er the riv - er, up the dell;___

Peace and rest to la - bor bring - ing, Chimes the bell, ___ chimes the bell.

Chimes, chimes the bell,___ chimes the bell.____

Chimes, chimes the bell, chimes the bell.____

Tawi' Kuruks

From "The Indians' Book" by
NATALIE CURTIS, published by
HARPER & BROTHERS

Study Song

PAWNEE TRIBE

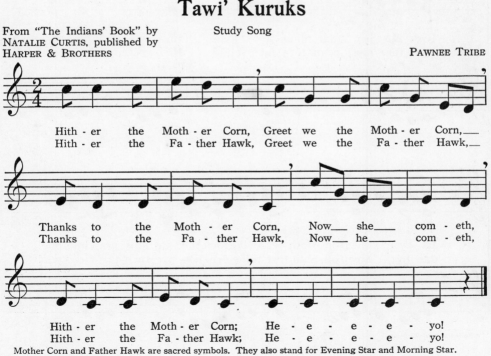

Hith - er   the   Moth - er Corn,   Greet   we   the   Moth - er   Corn,__
Hith - er   the   Fa - ther Hawk,   Greet   we   the   Fa - ther   Hawk,__

Thanks   to   the   Moth - er   Corn,   Now__ she__   com - eth,
Thanks   to   the   Fa - ther   Hawk,   Now__ he__   com - eth,

Hith - er   the   Moth - er   Corn;   He - e - e - e - yo!
Hith - er   the   Fa - ther   Hawk;   He - e - e - e - yo!

Mother Corn and Father Hawk are sacred symbols. They also stand for Evening Star and Morning Star.

Eiapopeia *
Reading Song

Translated from the German

BOHEMIAN FOLK SONG

Andante sostenuto, con tenerezza

Ei - a - po - pei - a,__ my__ ba - by, sleep on,   Moth - er__ is
Rest thee, my__ ba - by, to__ slum-ber be - guiled, Peace-ful - ly

rock-ing__her__ dar - ling__a - lone.   Ei - a - hei - a,____
rest__thee, my__beau-ti - ful__child.   Ei - a - hei - a,____

ba - by,__ sleep on, Moth-er__will__rock thee a - lone, pre-cious one!
dar - ling,__ sleep on, Shut fast thine eye - lids, my__own pre-cious one!

Pronounce i-ah-po-pi-ah.

Dream Song

Study Song - School Choir

WALTER DE LA MARE

W. OTTO MIESSNER

Slowly, with expression

Sun-light, moon-light, twi - light, star-light, Gleam-ing
Elf-light, bat - light, touch wood light, toad-light, And the

Sun - light, moon - light, twi - light, star - light, Gleam-ing
Elf - light, bat - light, 'touch wood light, toad - light, And the

at the close of day, Hoot - owls call - ing,
sea a gloom of gray, Fac - es smil - ing,

at the close of day,
sea a gloom of gray,

In a wood of oak and may.___
In a world of far a - way.___

Cool dews fall - ing, In a wood of may.___
Dreams be - guil - ing, In a world a - way.___

The Primrose

Rote Song - School Choir

Frederick H. Martens

Edvard Grieg

The prim-rose is the gift of spring

To us who now a - wait her,

A to - ken true of days to come,

And ros - es bloom-ing la - ter.

Yet though the summer blaze with flow'rs And au - tumn gold - en glows,

The spring's the fair-est time of all When first the prim-rose blows.

Edvard Grieg

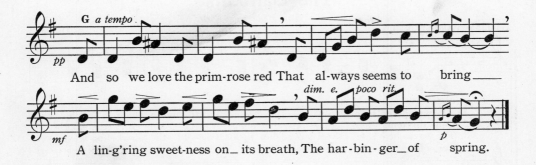

And so we love the prim-rose red That al-ways seems to bring____

A lin-g'ring sweet-ness on__ its breath, The har-bin-ger__ of spring.

Spirit of the Summer-Time

Reading Song

WILLIAM ALLINGHAM

OLD IRISH FOLK SONG

1. Oh spir-it sweet of____ sum - mer - time,
   Bring back the ros - es____ to____ the dells, The swal-low from her
2. Bring back the sing - ing,__ bring__ the scent
   Of mead-ow-lands at____ dew - y prime; Oh! bring a-gain my

dis - tant clime, The hon-ey-bee from__ drow - sy cells.
heart's__ con - tent, Thou spir-it sweet of____ sum - mer - time.

The Daffodils
Study Song

William Wordsworth

E. Hermes

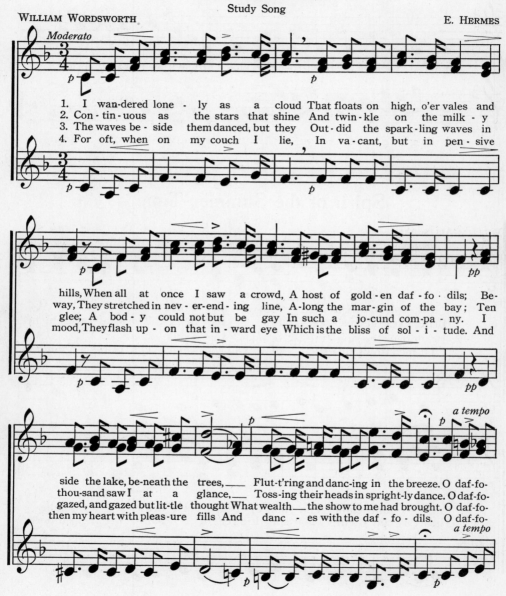

1. I wan-dered lone - ly as a cloud That floats on high, o'er vales and hills, When all at once I saw a crowd, A host of gold - en daf - fo - dils; Be - side the lake, be - neath the trees, ___ Flut-t'ring and danc-ing in the breeze. O daf-fo-

2. Con - tin - uous as the stars that shine And twin - kle on the milk - y way, They stretched in nev - er - end - ing line, A-long the mar - gin of the bay; Ten thou-sand saw I at a glance. ___ Toss-ing their heads in spright-ly dance. O daf-fo-

3. The waves be - side them danced, but they Out - did the spark - ling waves in glee; A bod - y could not but be gay In such a jo-cund com-pa - ny. I gazed, and gazed but lit-tle thought What wealth ___ the show to me had brought. O daf-fo-

4. For oft, when on my couch I lie, In va - cant, but in pen - sive mood, They flash up - on that in - ward eye Which is the bliss of sol - i - tude. And then my heart with pleas-ure fills And danc - es with the daf - fo - dils. O daf-fo-

dils, O daf - fo - dils, A host of gold - en daf - fo - dils. O

O daf - fo -

daf - fo - dils, O daf - fo - dils, A host of___ gold - en___ daf - fo - dils.

dils,___ O daf - fo - dils.___ A host of gold - en,

In the Patio

Reading Song

ALDIS DUNBAR

SPANISH FOLK SONG

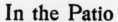

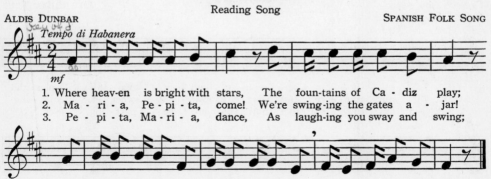

Tempo di Habanera

1. Where heav-en is bright with stars, The foun-tains of Ca - diz play;
2. Ma - ri - a, Pe - pi - ta, come! We're swing-ing the gates a - jar!
3. Pe - pi - ta, Ma - ri - a, dance, As laugh-ing you sway and swing;

And sil -ver the star-light, gold-en the fire-light, Min-gle with toss -ing spray.
For un-der the star-light, gyp-sies are sing-ing, Strik-ing the gay gui - tar!
The mu-sic draws near-er, sweet-er and clear-er, Un-der the stars of spring!

Spring Night

Reading Song

BLISS CARMAN

EDWARD ELGAR
"Salut d'Amour"

Andantino

In the __ won-drous star-sown night, __ In the __ first sweet warmth of spring,

May be repeated humming

sing! _____

I lie a-wake and __ lis-ten, lis-ten To hear the __ glad earth sing, sing, sing!

Isalei*

Study Song

Free translation by
ANNE LANDSBURY BECK

OLD FIJIAN TUNE

Moderato, steady rhythm

(p) 1. To my Is-land where dream-y sun-lit wa-ters Dance and
(f) 2. In your pres-ence the song-birds war-ble sweet-er, Arch-ing
(pp) 3. I am sad ___ that now you are de-part-ing, For your

spar-kle, and play-ful waves the spray flings; ___ To my
rain-bows make col-ors rich as treas-ure; ___ State-ly
friend-ship doth send dull thought a-wing-ing; ___ With my

poco a poco *cresc.*

vil - lage, where cor - al beach - es beck - on, Straight you
palm trees, that waft us gen - tle breez - es, Fan the
frail____ ca - noe I can - not fol - low, Come you

sailed____ and an - chored to my heart - strings.
moon - rays that light the hours for pleas - ure.
back____ and keep my heart a - sing - ing.

mf
I - sa - le - i____ sail not far a - way____ My best loved

mf

friend from you I can - not part;____ In my ca - noe,____ There's a place for

you,____ In my vil - lage a wel - come in each heart.

*Pronounced ē-sä-lāy-ē. Isalei is the Fijian word for "farewell."

FRED GEIB PLAYING THE TUBA

Theme
The "Dragon" motive, from "Siegfried"

TUBAS   RICHARD WAGNER

134

Swing Low, Sweet Chariot

Reading Song

TRADITIONAL

NEGRO SPIRITUAL

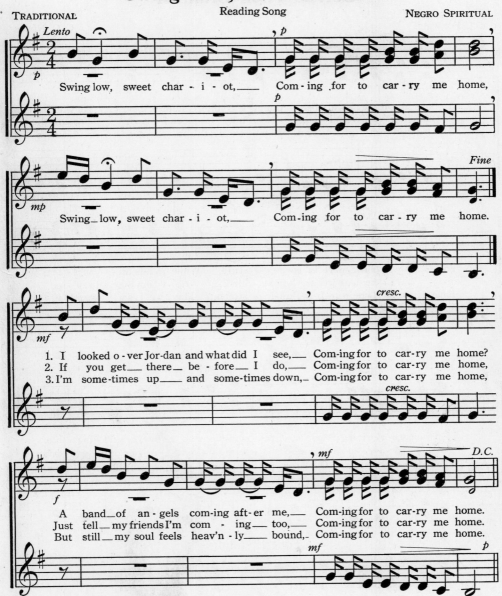

Swing low, sweet char-i-ot,___ Com-ing for to car-ry me home,

Swing_low, sweet char-i-ot,___ Com-ing for to car-ry me home.

1. I looked o-ver Jor-dan and what did I see,___ Com-ing for to car-ry me home?
2. If you get___ there be-fore___ I do,___ Com-ing for to car-ry me home,
3. I'm some-times up___ and some-times down,___ Com-ing for to car-ry me home,

A band_of an-gels com-ing aft-er me,___ Com-ing for to car-ry me home.
Just tell___ my friends I'm com-ing too,___ Com-ing for to car-ry me home.
But still___ my soul feels heav'n-ly___ bound,_ Com-ing for to car-ry me home.

Soft Is Their Slumber

Reading Song

A. J. FOXWELL

C. G. NEEFE

Slow and smooth

1. Soft is their slum - ber, Count - less their num - ber, All who have
2. Once they con - tend - ed, Now toil is end - ed, Far in the
3. Life still in mo - tion, Down to death's o - cean Sweeps us a -

no - bly borne part in earth - ly strife;__ While friends are weep - ing,
dis - tance earth's cares are left be - hind;__ He whom they trust - ed
long__ in Time's swift - ly - flow - ing stream; May we so spend it,

Now they are sleep - ing, Wait - ing the sum - mons to__ nev - er - end - ing life.
All has ad - just - ed, Those who be - lieve Him will__ ev - er safe - ty find.
That when we end__ it, Our hap - py spir - its may__ wake to bliss su - preme.

Tone Blending

The Rhyme of the Country Road

Rote Song - School Choir

EMMA ENDICOTT MAREAN

LEO SOWERBY

In moderate march time

mf

1. Oh, the life one leads a - tramp - ing, A -
2. Oh, the sights one sees a - tramp - ing, The___
3. Oh, the thoughts one thinks a - tramp - ing, The___

tramp - ing___ a coun-try road, A - far - ing in gyp - sy
green,___ wild___ things that___ grow, The gleam of the tall red
joy___ of___ the coun-try road, A - far - ing in gyp - sy

fash - ion With___ nev - er a gyp - sy's___
lil - y, The___ tan - gle of ferns be -
fash - ion With___ nev - er a gyp - sy's___

load; Set___ free as the winds in___ spring - time,___
low; The___ gay,___ glad___ life of the tree - tops,___
load; De - light___ in the world of___ beau - ty, A

Heart - glad as the day is long, Re - joic - ing in rain or___
Shad - ows that___ slow - ly fall, The___ long, still___ slope of the
rap - ture of___ love and praise And a will to make life the___

sun - shine, In___ tune with the rob - in's song!
mead - ows, And___ blue sky___ o - ver all!
tru - er For the glo - ry of com - mon days!

The Bells

Reading Song

EDGAR ALLAN POE, adapted

HALFDAN KJERULF

1. Hear the sledg-es with the bells, Sil-ver, sil-ver bells,___
2. Hear the mel-low wed-ding bells, Gold-en, gold-en bells,___
3. Hear the loud a-lar-um bells, Bra-zen, bra-zen bells,___

1. Hear the sledg-es with the sil-ver, sil-ver bells,
2. Hear the mel-low wed-ding bells, the gold-en bells,
3. Hear the loud a-lar-um bells, the bra-zen bells,

What a world of mer-ri-ment their mel-o-dy fore-tells;___
What a world of hap-pi-ness their har-mo-ny fore-tells;___
What a tale of ter-ror, now, their tur-bu-len-cy tells;___

What a world of mer-ri-ment their mel-o-dy fore-tells;
What a world of hap-pi-ness their har-mo-ny fore-tells;
What a tale of ter-ror, now, their tur-bu-len-cy tells;

How they tin-kle with de-light In the i-cy air of night,
Through the balm-y air of night, How they ring out their de-light,
In the start-led ear of night, How they scream out their af-fright!

How they tin-kle, tin-kle, tin-kle, Tin-kle, tin-kle, tin-kle, tin-kle,
Chim-ing, chim-ing, chim-ing, chim-ing, Chim-ing, chim-ing, chim-ing, chim-ing,
Clang-ing, clang-ing, clang-ing, clang-ing, Clang-ing, clang-ing, clang-ing, clang-ing,

Note: The interpretation and tone color of each stanza should be in keeping with the text.

Keep - ing time,__ keep - ing time,__ In__ a sort of rhyme,
How it dwells,__ how it swells,__ To__the chim - ing bells,
How they clang,__ how they roar,__ Hor - ror they out-pour,

Keep - ing, keep - ing time, In a sort of Ru - nic rhyme;
How it dwells and swells, To the chim - ing of the bells;
How they clang and roar! What a hor - ror they out-pour;

In_____ a_____ sort of Ru - nic rhyme!
To_____ the_____ chim - ing of_____ the bells!
What_____ a_____ hor - ror they_____ out - pour!

Keep - ing time,_____ In a sort of Ru - nic rhyme!
How it swells,_____ To the chim - ing of the bells!
How they roar,_____ What a hor - ror they out - pour!

Tone Blending

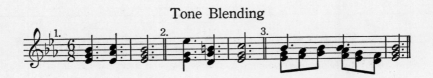

Celestial Aïda
Theme, from "Aïda"

A. GHISLANZONI (translated)

GIUSEPPE VERDI

GIUSEPPE VERDI

Ce - les - tial A - ï - da,___ Vi - sion tran-

scend - ent___ Beau - ty___ im - mor - tal,

Spir - it___ di - vine! Though still___ en-

slav - ed,___ I will re-deem thee, Save thee, and make thee for-ev-er mine!

Anvil Chorus, from " Il Trovatore "
Reading Song

TRADITIONAL

GIUSEPPE VERDI

God of the na - tions, in glo - ry en - thron-ed, Up-on our loved

coun - try Thy bless - ing pour; Guide us and guard us from strife in the

fu - ture, Let Peace dwell a - mong us for ev - er - more!

Proud - ly our ban - ner now gleams with gold - en

lus - ter! Bright - er each star____ shines____ in the glo - rious

clus - ter! Hail! Hail! Hail! ban - ner of the free! And Peace and

Un - ion, and Peace and Un - ion, through-out our hap - py land!

The Ancient Polonaise
Study Song

NANCY BYRD TURNER   POLISH FOLK SONG

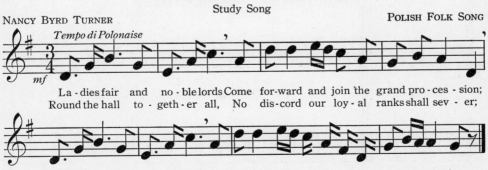

La - dies fair and no - ble lords Come for-ward and join the grand pro - ces - sion;
Round the hall to - geth - er all, No dis - cord our loy - al ranks shall sev - er;

Bend the knee be - fore your king, All ea - ger your loy-al-ty to give ex - pres-sion.
Lord of right di - rect our might, For Po-land and lib - er - ty we stand for - ev - er.

Only One
Reading Song

GEORGE COOPER

HORATIO PARKER

Hun-dreds of stars in the pret-ty sky, Hun-dreds of shells on the

shore___ to - geth - er, Hun-dreds of birds that go sing - ing by,

Hun-dreds of bees in the sun - ny weath-er. Hun-dreds of dew-drops to

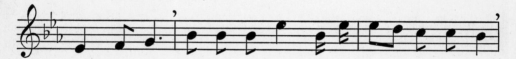

greet the dawn, Hun-dreds of lambs in the pur - ple clo - ver,

Hun-dreds of but - ter-flies on___ the lawn, But on - ly one moth-er___ The

wide world o - ver, On - ly one___ moth-er___ The wide world o - ver.

Awaking

Reading Song

From *The Aeolian Collection*

BOHEMIAN FOLK SONG

1. Wilt thou sleep for - ev - er,_____ Eye-lids o - pen___ nev - er,
2. Now from slum - ber___ tak - en,_____ Let thy blue eyes___ wak - en!
3. Up the sun ad - vanc - es,_____ With its gold - en___ glanc - es,

Child with cheeks the___ rose a - dorn - ing?___ Long a - go___ the___ birds of morn - ing___
All is read - y___ for my dear - est,___Bread and milk_when___thou ap-pear - est;___
Shin-ing on___ thy___ bed so bright-ly,___ Kiss-ing mouth and cheek so light - ly;___

Sweet-est songs did raise_____ To their Mak - er's___ praise.
Yet thou stay - est, child,_____ Still in slum - ber___ mild.
In its cheer - ing ray,_____ Wak - en in - to___ day.

Bird Calls

Reading Song - School Choir

From *Poetry of the Seasons*

MARSHALL BARTHOLOMEW

Andantino

1. Oh, see that gray bird in the old __ ap - ple tree That is
here comes an - oth - er, he's taw - ny and white; Ev - er
there comes an - oth - er, and where do you think This gay
now it is night, in the world all is still, Not a

snow - y with blos - soms as it __ can __ be. If I ask __ her __ name she will
blithe - ly he whis - tles from morn to __ night. He is ver - y __ shy and keeps
fel - low will lin - ger to swing and __ prink? On a clo - ver __ top, where the
glim - mer of sun - shine up - on __ the __ hill, Then a sud - den __ whis - tle, in

I* *After 1st verse* D.S.

sing to me. She heard me and ans - wers, "Phe - be, __ Phe - be." 2. Now __
out of sight, His name he tells clear - ly, __
cat - tle drink, He chat - ters his name, __
ac - cents shrill, A bird gives his name, __

II *After 2nd verse*   I   II   D.S. Tutti   III *After 3rd verse*

a tempo

"Bob Bob White," __ "Phe - be," __ "Bob Bob White." 3. Now __ "Bob - o - link, Bob - o - link,"

II   I   III   D.S. Tutti

"Bob Bob White," __ "Phe - be", __ "Bob - o - link, Bob - o - link." 4. Lo __

IV *After 4th verse*   III   II   I

"Whip - poor - will," "Bob - o - link, Bob - o - link," "Bob Bob White," __ "Phe - be."

* I, II, III, IV, indicate different groups of singers.

Roller Skating

Study Song - School Choir

Norma Verbeck

Adolf Weidig

Rather fast and steady

Oh, bring your roll - er skates_____ And roll - ing we will
We cer - tain - ly have fun_____ Each eve - ning aft - er

Oh, bring your roll - er skates_____ And
We cer - tain - ly have fun_____ Each

go,_____ Up and down the side - walk, Hur - ry don't be
tea;_____ We some - times skate in cir - cles, Play - ing tag, you

roll - ing we will go,_____ Up and down the side - walk, Hur - ry don't be
eve - ning aft - er tea; We some - times skate in cir - cles, Play - ing tag, you

slow._____ Ma - ry's there and How - ard, too, And Hel - en, Ger - trude,
see;_____ Hel - en's "it," we all skate fast, And then she catch - es

slow, be slow,_____ Ma - ry's there and How - ard too, And Hel - en and
see, you see;_____ Hel - en's "it," we all skate fast, And then_____ she

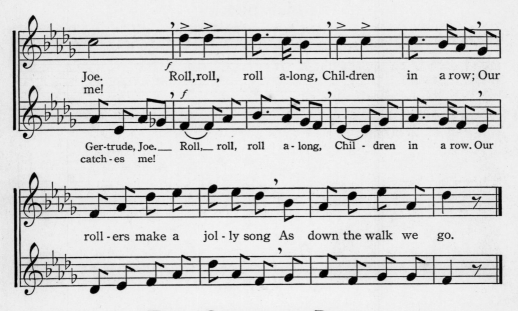

Joe. Roll, roll, roll a-long, Chil-dren in a row; Our
me!

Ger-trude, Joe.__ Roll,__ roll, roll a-long, Chil - dren in a row. Our
catch - es me!

roll - ers make a jol - ly song As down the walk we go.

Early Summer in Russia

Reading Song

ALDIS DUNBAR

CONSTANTIN SHVEDOFF

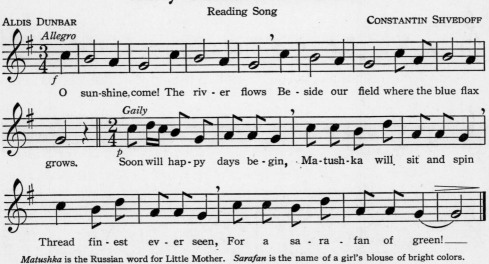

Allegro

O sun-shine, come! The riv - er flows Be - side our field where the blue flax

Gaily

grows. Soon will hap - py days be - gin, Ma - tush - ka will sit and spin

Thread fin - est ev - er seen, For a sa - ra - fan of green!__

Matushka is the Russian word for Little Mother. *Sarafan* is the name of a girl's blouse of bright colors.

Clouds

Reading Song

FREDERICK H. MARTENS

FRANÇOIS FREDERIC CHOPIN

FRANÇOIS FREDERIC CHOPIN

Mist in the vale and wild geese on

high, De - spair - ing the pine trees

mourn-ful are sigh - ing, O - ver the

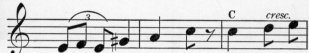

fields the sun-light is dy - ing, Dark are the heav - ens and cloud - ed the

sky. While na - ture, all shroud - ed, Her face is de - ny - ing, Yet we well

know that the clouds of to - day_____ A gold - en mor-row sweeps a - way.

The Spirit of the Birch

Study Song - School Choir

Arthur Ketchum

W. Otto Miessner

I am the danc-er of the wood,_____ I

I am the danc-er of the

shim-mer in the sol - i - tude;_____ Men_____

wood,_____ I shim-mer in the sol - i - tude;_____

call me, "Birch - tree,"_____ yet I know In oth - er

Men call me "Birch - tree," yet_____

days_____ It was___ not___ so.___

I know in oth - er___ days___ It was not___ so.___

4 G   b
I am a Dry-ad___ slim and white___ Who

4

danced___ too long one sum - mer night.___

a

Who danced too long one sum - mer night.___ But the

f

Cap - tive I

dawn found and pris - oned me; Cap - tive, I moan___ my

moan!_____ Yet, let the wood-wind flutes be-

lib - er - ty!_____

gin_____ Their elf - in mu - sic light and

Yet, let the wood-wind flutes be - gin_____ Their

thin;_____ I sway, I bend,__ And

elf - in mu - sic light and thin;__ Re - treat, ad - vance,

ev - er-more I dance,__ I_____ dance!_____

Yet ev - er-more I dance, I dance!_____

The Spanish Gypsy*

Study Song

From the Spanish

SPANISH FOLK SONG

I dance the bright bo - le - ro, Each vil-lage maid-en loves my
I am the Span-ish gyp - sy, I roam our hap-py hills a-

lay, When in vine-yards grapes do rip - en, And the
mong, With my cas-ta-nets a - click - ing, On my

fruit grows sweet - er ev - 'ry day. I dance the bright bo-
lips a blithe - some___ song. I am the Span-ish

le - ro, With fly - ing feet And song so gay.
gyp - sy, And dance I must my whole life long.___

*May be sung as a unison song.

Procession of Flowers

Reading Song

ANONYMOUS

ROSSETTER G. COLE

With graceful movement

mp

Sing, sing, lil - y bells ring, The blos-soms are com-ing to

town,___ Dai - sies and lil - ies and daf - fy - down - dil - lies,

Each in a sweet new gown.__ Sing, sing, lil - y bells ring, The

blos-soms are com-ing to town,__ Pan - sy and mi-gnon-ette,

Mar - i - gold, vio - let Each in a rich new gown.__

In Summer-time When Flow'rs Do Spring

Reading Song

TRADITIONAL

SELLENGER'S ROUND

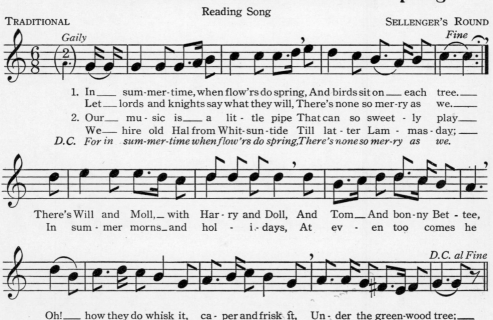

1. In __ sum-mer-time, when flow'rs do spring, And birds sit on __ each tree.__
   Let __ lords and knights say what they will, There's none so mer-ry as we.__
2. Our __ mu - sic is __ a lit - tle pipe That can so sweet - ly play __
   We __ hire old Hal from Whit-sun-tide Till lat - ter Lam - mas-day; __

D.C. For in sum-mer-time when flow'rs do spring, There's none so mer-ry as we.

There's Will and Moll,__ with Har - ry and Doll, And Tom__ And bon-ny Bet-tee,
In sum - mer morns__ and hol - i - days, At ev - en too comes he

D.C. al Fine

Oh! __ how they do whisk it, ca - per and frisk it, Un - der the green-wood tree; __
And __ then we do skip it, ca - per and trip it, Un - der the green-wood tree; __

The Toadstool

Study Song - School Choir

Oliver Wendell Holmes

William Lester

Moderato con espressione

And springs in the shade of the
There's a thing that grows by the faint-ing flower And

la - dy's bower, The lil - y shrinks and the rose turns pale When they

feel its breath in the sum - mer gale, And the tu - lip curls its
Tra la!

più allegro, leggiero
crisply, with grace

leaves in pride, And the blue - eyed vi - o - let starts a - side; But the
tra, la!
The blue-eyed vi - o - let starts a - side; But the

Kubey-Rembrandt Studios, Philadelphia

W. M. KINCAID	DANIEL BONADE	J. WALTER GUETTER	JOSEPH WOLFE	MARCEL TABUTEAU
Flute	*Clarinet*	*Bassoon*	*English Horn*	*Oboe*

PRINCIPALS OF THE WOODWIND SECTION
THE PHILADELPHIA ORCHESTRA

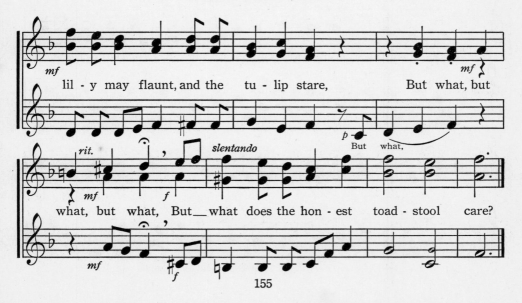

lil - y may flaunt, and the tu - lip stare, But what, but

what, but what, But__ what does the hon - est toad - stool care?

Rory O'Moore

Rote Song

Samuel Lover

OLD IRISH AIR

Lively, but not too fast

Young Ro-ry O' Moore court-ed Kath-a-leen Bawn, He was bold as a hawk, and she

soft as the dawn; He wished in his heart pret-ty Kath-leen to please, And he

thought the best way to do that was to tease. "Now, Ro-ry, be ai-sy," sweet

Kath-leen would cry, Re-proof on her lip but a smile in her eye, "With your

tricks I don't know, in troth, what I'm a-bout, Faith, you've teas'd till I've put on my

cloak in-side out." "Oh, Jew-el!" says Ro-ry, "That same is the way you've

trat-ed my heart for this man-y a day. And 'tis plazed that I am and why

not to be sure? For 'tis all for good luck," says bold Ro-ry O' Moore.

Time Enough

Rote Song

BERTON BRALEY · GEORGE W. CHADWICK

We've a veined on - yx block for a sleep - ing room clock, We've a

din - ing room clock that has gongs in; We've a kitch-en clock, too, and a

cuck - oo, brand new, I can't say which room that be - longs in. We've a

lu - mi-nous clock, an e - lec - tri-cal clock, And a clock with eight bells it can

chime with; But we hope that no harm meets our

dol - lar a - larm, For that is the clock we keep time with!

If Any Little Word of Ours

AUTHOR UNKNOWN

Reading Song

HECTOR MacCARTHY

If an-y lit-tle word of ours Can make one heart the light-er; If an-y lit-tle song of ours Can make one heart the bright-er; heart the bright-er speak that lit-tle word, And God help us speak, God help us speak that lit-tle word, And take our bit of sing-ing, And drop it in some low-ly vale, And

ring ing.

set the ech-oes, set the ech-oes ding dong ding.

rall.

rall.

The Little Turtle

Rote Song - School Choir

VACHEL LINDSAY*   JOHN ALDEN CARPENTER

Animato

There was a lit-tle tur-tle, He lived in a box.__ He swam in a

pud-dle, He climbed up-on the rocks.   He snapped at a mos-

qui-to. He snapped at a flea.____ He snapped at a min-now, And

he snapped at me.____ He caught the mos-qui-to, He caught the flea, He

cresc.

caught the min-now; But he did-n't catch me.____

* From *Silver Pennies* by Blanche Jennings Thompson. By permission of The Macmillan Company, publishers.

Battle Hymn of the Republic

JULIA WARD HOWE   Reading Song   WILLIAM STEFFE

Mine — eyes have seen the glo - ry of the com - ing of the Lord: He is
In the beau - ty of the lil - ies Christ was born a - cross the sea, With a

tramp - ing out the vin - tage where the grapes of wrath are stored: He hath
glo - ry in His bos - om that trans - fig - ures you and me: As He

loosed the fate - ful light - ning of His ter - ri - ble swift sword; His
died to make men ho - ly let us die to make men free, While

truth — is march - ing on.
God — is march - ing on. Glo - ry! Glo - ry Hal - le - lu - jah!

Glo - ry! Glo - ry Hal - le - lu - jah! Glo - ry! Glo - ry Hal - le -

lu - jah! His truth is march - ing on.

National Hymn

Reading Song

D. C. ROBERTS

GEORGE W. WARREN

1. God of our fa-thers, whose al-might-y
2. Thy love di - vine hath led us in the
3. From war's a - larms, from dead-ly pes - ti-
4. Re - fresh Thy peo - ple on their toil-some

hand_____ Leads forth in beau - ty all the star - ry
past;_____ In this free land our lot by Thee is
lence,_____ Be Thy strong arm our ev - er sure de-
way._____ Lead us from night to nev - er - end - ing

band_____ Of shin - ing worlds in splen - dor through the
cast._____ Be Thou our rul - er, guard-ian, guide, and
fence;_____ Thy true re - li - gion in our hearts in-
day;_____ Fill all our lives with love and grace di-

Used by permission of The Century Company.

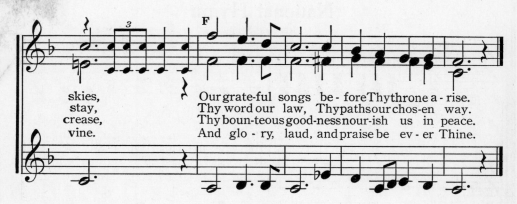

skies,   Our grate-ful songs be-fore Thy throne a-rise.
stay,   Thy word our law, Thy paths our chos-en way.
crease,   Thy boun-teous good-ness nour-ish us in peace.
vine.   And glo - ry, laud, and praise be ev - er Thine.

America, the Beautiful

Reading Song

KATHARINE LEE BATES   SAMUEL A. WARD

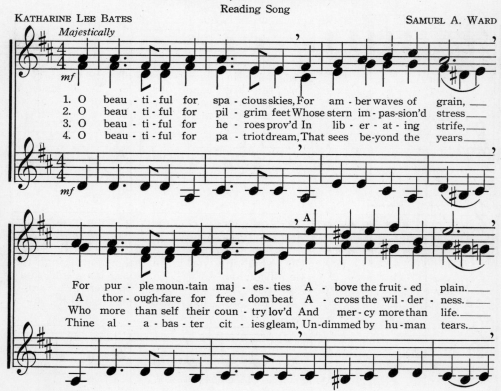

1. O beau - ti - ful for spa - cious skies, For am - ber waves of grain, ___
2. O beau - ti - ful for pil - grim feet Whose stern im - pas-sion'd stress ___
3. O beau - ti - ful for he - roes prov'd In lib - er - at - ing strife, ___
4. O beau - ti - ful for pa - triot dream, That sees be-yond the years ___

For pur - ple moun-tain maj - es - ties A - bove the fruit - ed plain. ___
A thor - ough-fare for free - dom beat A - cross the wil - der - ness. ___
Who more than self their coun - try lov'd And mer - cy more than life. ___
Thine al - a - bas - ter cit - ies gleam, Un-dimmed by hu - man tears. ___

A - mer - i - ca! A - mer - i - ca! God shed His grace on thee,____
A - mer - i - ca! A - mer - i - ca! God mend thine ev - 'ry flaw,____
A - mer - i - ca! A - mer - i - ca! May God thy gold re - fine ____
A - mer - i - ca! A - mer - i - ca! God shed His grace on thee,____

And crown thy good with broth - er - hood From sea to shin - ing sea.
Con - firm thy soul in self - con - trol, Thy lib - er - ty in law.
Till all suc - cess be no - ble - ness, And ev - 'ry gain di - vine.
And crown thy good with broth - er - hood From sea to shin - ing sea.

Deep River

Reading Song

NEGRO SPIRITUAL

Humming

Hm.____ Hm.____

Deep ____ riv - er, My home is o - ver Jor - dan,____

Hm.____ Hm.____

Deep ____ riv - er, Lord, I want to cross o - ver in - to camp ground.

The Star-Spangled Banner
Service Version

FRANCIS SCOTT KEY

JOHN STAFFORD SMITH

1. Oh,— say! can you see,— by the dawn's ear - ly light, What so proud-ly we
2. On the shore, dim-ly seen through the mists of the deep, Where the foe's haugh-ty
3. Oh,— thus be it ev - er— when— free-men shall stand Be - tween their loved

hailed at the twilight's last gleaming? Whose broad stripes and bright stars through the
host in dread si - lence re - pos - es, What is that which the breeze, o'er the
homes and the war's des - o - la - tion! Blest with vic - t'ry and peace, may the

per - il - ous fight, O'er the ram - parts we watched were so gal - lant - ly
tow - er - ing steep, As it fit - ful - ly blows, half con - ceals, half dis-
heav'n - res - cued land Praise the Pow'r that hath made and pre - served us a

streaming? And the rock-ets' red glare, the bombs burst-ing in air,— Gave proof through the
clos-es? Now it catch-es the gleam of the morn-ing's first beam, In full glo-ry re-
na-tion! Then— con-quer we must, when our cause it is just; And— this be our

3rd verse *maestoso*   CHORUS

night— that our flag was still there. Oh,— say, does that— Star-Span-gled
flect-ed now— shines on the stream; 'Tis the Star-Span-gled— Ban-ner, oh,
mot-to: "In— God is our trust!" And the Star-Span-gled— Ban-ner, in

Ban-ner, yet— wave O'er the land— of the free and the home of the brave?
long may it— wave O'er the land— of the free and the home of the brave!
tri-umph shall— wave O'er the land— of the free and the home of the brave!

broaden

America

SAMUEL FRANCIS SMITH

HENRY CAREY

1. My coun - try! 'tis of thee, Sweet land of lib - er - ty,
2. My na - tive coun - try, thee, Land of the no - ble free,
3. Let mu - sic swell the breeze, And ring from all the trees
4. Our fa - thers' God, to Thee, Au - thor of lib - er - ty,

Of thee I sing; Land where my fa - thers died, Land of the
Thy name I love; I love thy rocks and rills; Thy woods and
Sweet Free-dom's song; Let mor - tal tongues a - wake, Let all that
To Thee we sing; Long may our land be bright With Free-dom's

Pil-grims' pride, From ev - 'ry__ moun - tain side Let__ free-dom ring.
tem - pled hills; My heart__with__ rap - ture thrills Like that a - bove.
breathe par-take, Let rocks__their__ si - lence break, The sound pro - long.
ho - ly light; Pro - tect__us__ by Thy might, Great God, our King.

The Violet

Study Song

HOFFMANN VON FALLERSLEBEN

H. G. NAGELI

Tell me, lit - tle flow - er, In this moss-y bow - er,
"Tim - id, but not lone - ly, I am lis - t'ning on - ly

Why thus sad and lone? Say of what thou dream - est,
To yon night- in - gale! While her song she trill - eth,

That to me thou seem - est So de - ject - ed grown.
And the si - lence fill - eth With its tune - ful wail."

Now Thank We All Our God

Reading Song

MARTIN RINKART

Chorale, "NUN DANKET"
JOHANN CRÜGER

Now thank we all our God, With heart and hands and voic - es, Who
O may this boun-teous God Through all our life be near__ us; With

won-drous things hath done, In whom His world re - joic - es; Who
ev - er joy - ful hearts, And bless - ed peace to cheer us; And

from our moth-er's arms Hath blessed us on our way With
keep us in His grace, And guide__ us when per - plexed, And

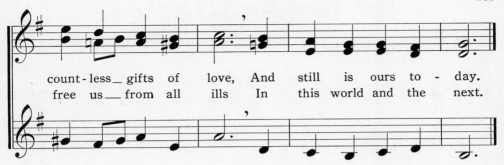

count - less_ gifts of love, And still is ours to - day.
free us__ from all ills In this world and the next.

Thankfulness

Reading Song

Adapted from the German
by ELEANOR GRAHAM

JOHANN SEBASTIAN BACH

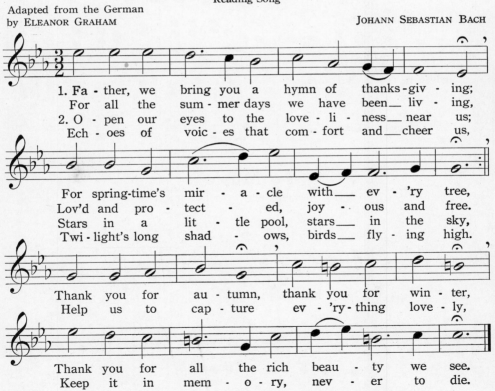

1. Fa - ther, we bring you a hymn of thanks-giv - ing;
For all the sum - mer days we have been__ liv - ing,
2. O - pen our eyes to the love - li - ness__ near us;
Ech - oes of voic - es that com - fort and__ cheer us,

For spring-time's mir - a - cle with__ ev - 'ry tree,
Lov'd and pro - tect - ed, joy - ous and free.
Stars in a lit - tle pool, stars__ in the sky,
Twi - light's long shad - ows, birds__ fly - ing high.

Thank you for au - tumn, thank you for win - ter,
Help us to cap - ture ev - 'ry-thing love - ly,

Thank you for all the rich beau - ty we see.
Keep it in mem - o - ry, nev - er to die.

My Own Fair Land

Reading Song

Adapted from the German
by Eleanor Alletta Chaffee

F. W. Sering

From the shores where o-ceans ring, To the hills where sea-sons sing,
Moun-tains are my broth-ers strong, And the o-cean's voice my song;

From the gran-ite rocks to the sand, the sand, This is mine, my own fair land.
And where far-off breez-es re-joice, re-joice, I can hear my coun-try's voice.

To Music

Reading Song - School Choir

From the German
by Eleanor Graham

Franz Schubert

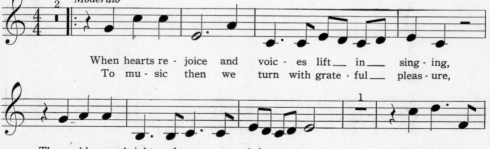

Moderato

When hearts re-joice and voic-es lift__ in__ sing-ing,
To mu-sic then we turn with grate-ful__ pleas-ure,

The world grows bright and sor-row fades a-way. The lilt of
For well we know what gifts we shall re-ceive, What peace of

Courtesy Braun & Cie, N. Y.

SAINT CECILIA, BY DOLCI

song, clear in— love-ly voic-es— ring-ing Can change the black of—
mind, ah, what joy be-yond all— meas-ure, For mu-sic makes the

night to mag-ic day,— The dark-est night— to gold-en day.
heart for-get to grieve, The lone-ly heart— for-get— to grieve.

The Night Is Past

Reading Song

The Modern Music Series

Arranged from KOHL

Moderato

The night is past; We wake— at last, For morn-ing now— re-
In qui-et trust We sank— to rest, In sleep fresh strength to

joic - es; To Thee a - bove, The God of love, We glad - ly
gath - er; Now glad - ly we Will work for Thee; Bless Thou our

raise our voic - es, We glad - ly raise our voic - es.
la - bor, Fa - ther, Bless Thou— our la - bor, Fa - ther.

Welcome, Mighty King

Reading Song

Paraphrased from the original
by EDA LOU WALTON

GEORGE FREDERICK HANDEL (1685-1759)
From the Oratorio "SAUL"

Wel - come, wel - come might - y___ king,___
Saul who con - quered on___ the___ plain___

Wel - come those who___ lau - rels bring, Wel - come Da - vid,
Wel - come to thy___ home a - gain, Wel - come, wel - come

hon - ored boy,___ He - ro of our___ pres - ent joy.
might - y king,___ Wel - come those who___ lau - rels bring.

Whoopee Ti Yi Yo

COWBOY SONG   Rote Song

As Sung by
KATE TAYLOR PARMLEY

1. As I was a-walk-ing one morn-ing for pleas-ure I
2. It's ear-ly in Spring that we round up the do-gies, We
3. It's whoop-ing and yell-ing and driv-ing the do-gies, And
4. Some boys they go up-on the trail just for pleas-ure, But

spied a cow-punch-er all rid-ing a-lone, His
mark them and brand them and bob off their tails; We
oh, how I wish you would on-ly go on; It's
that's where they get it most aw-ful-ly wrong; You

hat was throwed back and his spurs was a-jing-ling, And
round up our hors-es, load up the chuck wag-on, And
whoop-ing and punch-ing, go on, lit-tle do-gies, You
have-n't an i-dea the trou-ble they give us, ____

as he ap-proach'd he was sing-ing this song;
then throw the do-gies out on-to the trail.
know that Wy-o-ming will be your new home.
While we go driv-ing them all____ a-long.

REFRAIN

Whoop-ee ti yi yo,____ git a-long, lit-tle do-gies,* It's

your mis-for-tune and none of my own; Whoop-ee ti yi yo,__ git a-

* Dō-gies: A motherless calf in a ranch herd.

long, lit- tle do - gies, You know that Wy - o - ming will be your new home.

Come, My Soul, Thou Must Be Waking

Reading Song

F. R. L. CANITZ

FRANZ JOSEPH HAYDN

1. Come, my soul, thou must be wak- ing, Now is
2. Pray that He may pros - per ev - er Each en-
3. Think that He thy ways be - hold - eth; He un-
4. On - ly God's free gifts a - buse not, Light re-

break- ing O'er the earth an - oth - er day;
deav - or, When thine aim is good and true;
fold - eth Ev - 'ry fault that lurks with - in;
fuse not, But His Spir - it's voice o - bey;

Come to Him who made this splen - dor, See thou
But that He may ev - er thwart thee, And con-
He the hid - den shame glossed o - ver Can dis-
Thou with Him shalt dwell, be - hold - ing Light en-

ren - der All thy fee - ble strength can pay.
vert thee, When thou e - vil would'st pur - sue.
cov - er, And dis - cern each deed of sin.
fold - ing All things in un - cloud - ed day.

The Hills of Tyrol

Reading Song

J. THÜMMEL

Moderato

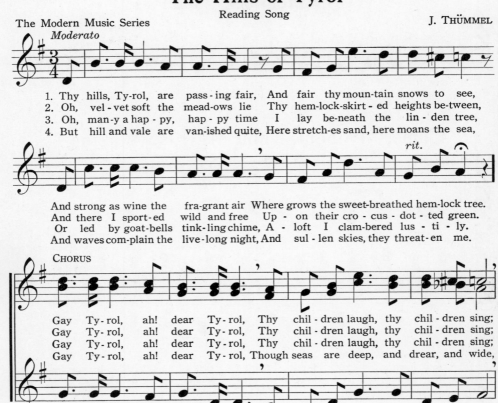

1. Thy hills, Ty-rol, are pass-ing fair, And fair thy moun-tain snows to see,
2. Oh, vel-vet soft the mead-ows lie Thy hem-lock-skirt-ed heights be-tween,
3. Oh, man-y a hap-py, hap-py time I lay be-neath the lin-den tree,
4. But hill and vale are van-ished quite, Here stretch-es sand, here moans the sea,

rit.

And strong as wine the fra-grant air Where grows the sweet-breathed hem-lock tree.
And there I sport-ed wild and free Up-on their cro-cus-dot-ted green.
Or led by goat-bells tink-ling chime, A-loft I clam-bered lus-ti-ly.
And waves com-plain the live-long night, And sul-len skies, they threat-en me.

CHORUS

Gay Ty-rol, ah! dear Ty-rol, Thy chil-dren laugh, thy chil-dren sing;
Gay Ty-rol, ah! dear Ty-rol, Thy chil-dren laugh, thy chil-dren sing;
Gay Ty-rol, ah! dear Ty-rol, Thy chil-dren laugh, thy chil-dren sing;
Gay Ty-rol, ah! dear Ty-rol, Though seas are deep, and drear, and wide,

Gay Ty-rol, ah! dear Ty-rol, Thy glad-ness shines in ev-'ry-thing.
Gay Ty-rol, ah! dear Ty-rol, Thy glad-ness shines in ev-'ry-thing.
Gay Ty-rol, ah! dear Ty-rol, Thy glad-ness shines in ev-'ry-thing.
Gay Ty-rol, ah! dear Ty-rol, I'll see a-gain thy moun-tain-side.

O Hemlock Tree

Study Song

From the German

GERMAN FOLK SONG

Moderato

1. O hem-lock tree, O hem-lock tree, How faith-ful are thy branch-es! Thou'rt
2. O hem-lock tree, O hem-lock tree, In truth I dear-ly love thee. How
3. O hem-lock tree, O hem-lock tree, A les-son thou dost teach me, That

green when sum-mer breez-es blow, And green'mid win-ter's drift-ing snow, O
oft at mer-ry Christ-mas tide Hast filled my heart with joy and pride! O
ev-er hope and con-stan-cy Will strength and com-fort give to me; O

hem-lock tree, O hem-lock tree, How faith-ful are thy branch-es!
hem-lock tree, O hem-lock tree, In truth I dear-ly love thee.
hem-lock tree, O hem-lock tree, A les-son thou dost teach me.

The Coin
Study Song

SARA TEASDALE *   PARKER BAILEY

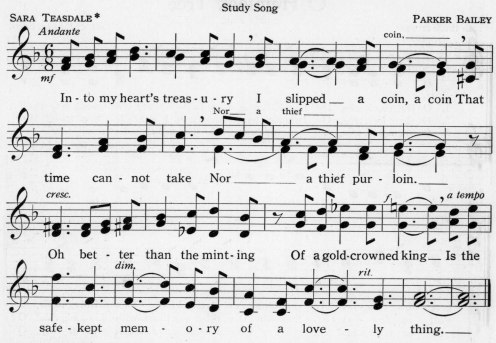

In - to my heart's treas - u - ry I slipped ___ a coin, a coin That

time can - not take Nor ___ a thief pur - loin. ___

Oh bet - ter than the mint - ing Of a gold-crowned king ___ Is the

safe - kept mem - o - ry of a love - ly thing. ___

*From *Flame and Shadow* by Sara Teasdale. By permission of The Macmillan Company, publishers.

Misieu' Banjo
Study Song *(Recorded)*

NEGRO-FRENCH FOLK SONG   Arranged by
                                              HENRI WEHRMANN

Gar - dé mi - lat' là, O Mi - sieu Ban - jo, Com - men li in - sol - ent!
See that young dark - y Play - ing the ban - jo, Is - n't he in - so - lent!

Cha - po co - té, O Mi - sieu Ban - jo, Ba - dine à la
Hat on one side, O Mi - sieu Ban - jo, Cane in right hand,

A LOUISIANA HOME IN OLD PLANTATION DAYS

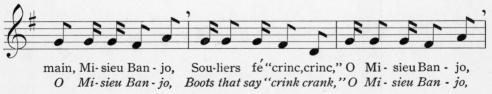

main, Mi‑sieu Ban‑jo,   Sou‑liers fé "crinc,crinc," O Mi‑sieu Ban‑jo,
O Mi‑sieu Ban‑jo,   Boots that say "crink crank," O Mi‑sieu Ban‑jo,

Gar‑dé mi‑lat' là,   O Mi‑sieu Ban‑jo, Com‑men li in‑sol‑ent!
See that young dark‑y   Play‑ing the ban‑jo,   Is‑n't he in‑so‑lent!

179

Giving

First stanza: MINOT J. SAVAGE
Second stanza: PERCIVAL CHUBB

Reading Song

M. VULPIUS, 1609
Arranged by F. W. SERING

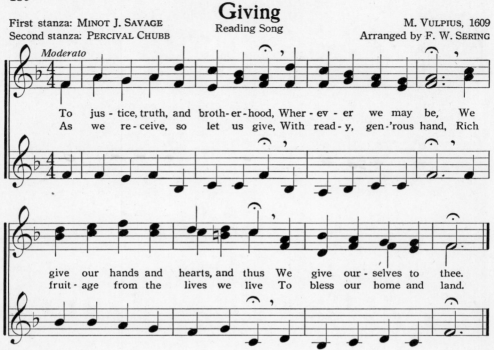

To jus-tice, truth, and broth-er-hood, Wher-ev-er we may be, We
As we re-ceive, so let us give, With read-y, gen-'rous hand, Rich

give our hands and hearts, and thus We give our-selves to thee.
fruit-age from the lives we live To bless our home and land.

A Spanish Christmas Carol

Reading Song

From the Spanish by
ELEANOR GRAHAM

MEXICAN FOLK TUNE*

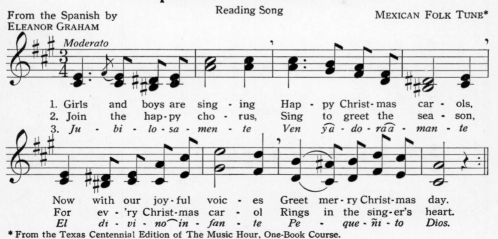

1. Girls and boys are sing-ing Hap-py Christ-mas car-ols,
2. Join the hap-py cho-rus, Sing to greet the sea-son,
3. *Ju - bi - lo-sa-men - te Ven ya - do - ráa - man - te*

Now with our joy-ful voic-es Greet mer-ry Christ-mas day.
For ev-'ry Christ-mas car-ol Rings in the sing-er's heart.
El di - vi - no in-fan - te Pe - que - ñi - to Dios.

*From the Texas Centennial Edition of The Music Hour, One-Book Course.

Homes are fill'd with laugh - ter, Arms are fill'd with pres - ents,
Trees and snow and pres - ents, Hol - ly in the win - dows,
Por él es - tá el cie - lo Sem - bra - do de es - tre - llas,

Earth is rul'd by glad - ness, Hearts are light and gay.
Make a mer - ry Christ - mas, Play a Christ-mas part.
Por él son tan be - llas, Las ob - ras de Dios.

Thoughts of Summer
Study Song

LOUISA ANNE TWOMLEY   EDWARD BAILEY BIRGE

1. The sum - mer time, the sum - mer time, The noon - tide of the year,
2. Oh! bless - ings on the sum - mer time! Its sun - shine and its flow'rs:
3. The lin - g'rings in the shad - y wood; The so - journs by the sea:
4. Oh! sum - mer time! sweet sum - mer time! The sum - mer sun and moon!

Oh! can there be a hu - man heart To which it is not dear?
I love its wide brown moor - land wastes, Its shad-ow y green-wood bowers.
The sea! oh, what a mag - ic sound Is that small word to me!
The joy - ous sounds of bird and bee, The mow - er's whis - tled tune!

A Song of Praise

Reading Song

Adapted from FOLLIOTT SANDFORD PIERPOINT
and REV. HORATIUS BONAR

FRIEDRICH SILCHER

1. For the beau - ty of the earth, For the glo - ry___
2. For the won - der of each hour Of the day___ and___
3. As the morn - ing light re - turns, As the sun___ with___

of the skies, For the love which from our___ birth___
of the night, Hill and vale, and tree and___ flow'r,___
splen - dor burns, Teach us still to turn to___ Thee,___

For the___ love___ which 'round us lies.___ Lord of all ac - cept our praise.
Sun and___ moon, and stars of light.___ Lord of all ac - cept our praise.
Ev - er___ bless - ed De - i - ty.___ Lord of all ac - cept our praise.

Questions for Thought and Discussion

1. Write down the names of the six songs which you would most enjoy singing at the closing exercises of the school term when parents and friends are present. Why are these songs appropriate for that occasion?

2. Name six songs which are not so suitable for such a program. Tell why.

3. Among the qualities which appeal to us in beautiful music are good melody, harmony, and rhythm. Which of these qualities appeals most strongly to you in each of the following songs: Stars of the Summer Night, p. 19; Christmas Stars, 53; Waltz in A-flat, 59; Hungarian Dancing Song, 84; April! April! 106; Gondoliera, 113; Spirit of the Summer-Time, 129; Spring Night, 132; The Rhyme of the Country Road, 137?

4. Can you identify the patterns of the following songs by indicating the phrases as A, B, A', etc.: The Nightingale's Complaint, p. 16; The Last Rose of Summer, 36; Weel May the Keel Row, 37; Largo from "New World" Symphony, 38; Let Songs of Praise Arise, 39; Theme from "Symphony Pathétique," 53; Boating Song, 64; Morning Hymn, 66; Green Holiday, 92; My Golden Fish, 101?

5. Can you find phrases in the above songs which are modified by: (a) ornamental tones; (b) change of key; (c) change of mode; (d) sequential repetition?

6. In which of the following part songs are the voices arranged chord-wise (harmonically)? Which are arranged with the voices in independent melodies (contrapuntally): Dawn at Carmel, p. 25; Leaves at Play, 34; Evening Song, 56; Market Day, 61; O Light-Bearing Star, 67; Eiapopeia, 126; Dream Song, 127; The Daffodils, 130?

7. Choose three words to describe each piece of music named below. You may refer, if you like, to the list of descriptive words on p. 75. The Primrose, p. 128; Largo, 105; Wandering, 91; Anvil Chorus, 140; Tarantella, 78; Evening Prayer, 82; Old Black Joe, 87; The Brooklet, 90; Farandole, 93; The Bolero, 94; Nocturne, from "Midsummer Night's Dream," 97; My Normandy, 110; Norway, 116; Sweet the Angelus Is Ringing, 122; Time Enough, 157; Deep River, 163; To a Wild Rose, MacDowell; Of a Tailor and a Bear, MacDowell; Swanee River, Foster.

8. Compare the following songs. Which one in each pair do you consider musically more interesting? Why?

   (a) Morning-Glories, p. 1, and Japanese National Anthem, p. 22.

   (b) O'er the Steppes, p. 28, and Italian Street Fair, p. 46.

   (c) Wioste Olowan, p. 31, and Dance of the Happy Spirits, p. 10.

   Why are the less musical of these songs nevertheless interesting for study?

9. Musical Interests

   (a) What is your favorite musical instrument? Why?

   (b) Do you like to hear other people play or sing? Have you attended any concerts this year?

   (c) When you listen to the radio, what kind of music do you prefer: dance music, jazz, symphony concerts, arias, familiar music, or novelties?

   (d) Do you take part in any music outside of school? Do you hear a good deal of music at home or elsewhere?

   (e) What do you plan to do with music next year in the Junior High School?

10. Three main reasons for studying music are discussed, and others are mentioned, on p. 74. Which of these apply especially to your music study this year?

GLOSSARY

Adagio. Slowly.

Alla marcia. In march style.

Allegretto. Diminutive of *allegro.* With animation, but not so fast as *allegro.*

Allegro. Lively, joyously, gayly, cheerfully.

Allegro moderato. Moderately fast.

Allegro non troppo. An *allegro* movement, but not too rapid.

Andante. Literally, to walk. A leisurely tempo.

Andante quasi Larghetto. *Andante* in the style of *Larghetto.*

Andantino. Diminutive of *andante.* Strictly speaking, faster than *andante,* although sometimes employed to indicate a slower movement.

Animato. Animatedly.

A tempo. In time.

Bolero. A rhythm in triple measure, associated with a characteristic Spanish dance.

Cantabile. Singable, melodious.

Cantando. In a singing style.

Con espressione. With expression.

Con moto. With motion, animatedly.

Con spirito. With spirit.

Con tenerezza. With tenderness.

Crescendo, cresc. Increasing in loudness.

Da Capo, D. C. Repeat from the beginning.

Dal Segno, D. S. From the sign. A direction to repeat from the sign 𝄋.

Di. By, with, of, for.

Diminuendo, dim. Diminishing in loudness.

Dolce. Sweetly.

Dolciss. Most sweetly.

Espressivo, espress. Expressively.

Farandole. A follow-the-leader dance popular in Southern France, usually accompanied with music in sextuple measure.

Finale. Final, concluding.

Fine. The end.

Forte, f. Loud.

Fortissimo, ff. Superlative of *forte,* very loud.

Grazioso. Gracefully.

Habanera. Rhythm in duple measure, associated with a characteristic Spanish dance.

Larghetto. Not quite so slow as *largo.*

Largo. A slow and solemn degree of movement.

Legato. Sustained, smoothly.

Leggiero. Lightly.

Lento. Slowly.

Lunga. A long pause.

Maestoso. Majestically.

Mazurka. Polish dance in triple measure.

Meno mosso. With less motion.

Mezzo forte, mf. Half loud.

Mezzo piano, mp. Half soft.

Moderato. Moderately.

Molto. Much.

Motive. The guiding theme or short characteristic melody which illustrates or describes personages, situations, or ideas in a music drama. Known also as *leit motif.*

Nocturne. Literally night piece; an evening song, or form of serenade.

Opera. A dramatic work in which the characters sing accompanied by orchestra.

Opus. A work, or composition.

Pathétique. In sad, wistful mood; emotionally moving.

Piano, p. Softly.

Pianissimo, pp. Superlative of *piano.* Very softly.

Pianisissimo, ppp. As softly as possible.

Più allegro. Faster at once.

Più lento. More slowly.

Poco. Somewhat, a little.

Polonaise. Polish dance in triple measure.

Rallentando, rall. Gradually becoming slower.

Ritardando, rit. Retard. Gradually becoming slower.

Ritenuto. Held back.

Rubato. Diminishing in one place and increasing in another; flexibility in tempo for purpose of expression.

Rustico. In simple, unaffected style.

Segno, 𝄋. Sign.

Sempre. Always.

Sforzando, sfz., sf. Accented.

Slentando. Gradual retard.

Sonatina. A work in sonata form with three or four movements, but shorter and simpler than a sonata.

Sostenuto. Sustained.

Symphony. An instrumental composition in three or four movements related in keys and contrasted in rhythms; hence a sonata for full orchestra.

Tarantella. Swift Italian dance in sextuple measure.

Tempo. Rate of speed.

Theme. A musical idea of a composition, a fragment of a melody which usually identifies the whole composition.

Tranquillo. Tranquilly.

Tutti. All sing.

Vivace. Vivaciously.

CLASSIFIED INDEX

185

ALPHABETIC INDEX

* These numbers refer to the catalogue of the R C A Manufacturing Company.

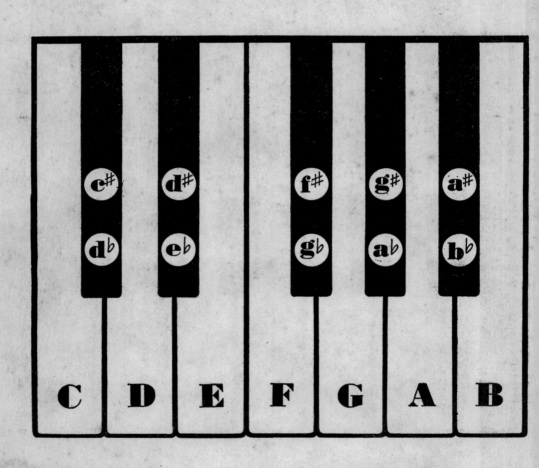